Low Stakes Nutrition

Kickstart Your Journey to Holistic Health

Created By: Sarah Hinrichsen

Photos By: Tyler Logan

Welcome!!

I'm Pumped You're Here!

Hi! I'm Sarah! I'm a performer (and a coffee addict) with a deep love for my family and friends and **a never-ending passion for all things nutrition**. I wholeheartedly believe that our bodies are our greatest blessing, and that nourishing them in a healthy way that fits our personal lifestyles is the single greatest gift we can give to ourselves.

I don't believe there is a "right" or "wrong" way to encourage our bodies to perform their best. All bodies, minds, and life experiences are different! That's why **I think it's CRAZY that we try and use one-size-fits-all approaches to medicine, weight loss, workout plans**... the list is never ending. I think a lot of this "one-size-fits-all" mentality comes from social media and constant comparison to others around us.... Sorry, I don't mean to start a Ted talk this early in the book!!

"Low Stakes Nutrition" was born out of countless conversations with friends, family, and random strangers in coffee shops. All of these convos were centered around their desires to up their nutrition game, but feeling intimidated by the vast amount of information out there, a fear of comparison, and a "but what if I fail?" mentality. My response to every single person has been the same: **"Lower the Stakes"**

Just because your favorite food blogger on IG had 3 hours to put together their banana blender pancakes and set up their plate for a photo shoot doesn't mean that you need that time or ambition to fuel your body correctly! **It doesn't have to be all or nothing!** Start by swapping one meal a week you would normally order out, to a salad thrown together with all the veggies in your refrigerator. When we get rid of that "all or nothing" mentality, our stakes immediately lower, and I have a feeling you'll notice a pretty immediate rise in success. Not to mention, **this gives you a chance to start really intentionally listening to your body**. You'll step away from "I can't have that Snickers bar because it's evil" and step toward "I could have a Snickers or an apple and I think the apple sounds more fueling right now!"

I've intentionally created this e-book **for anyone who is ready to take a first step toward holistic health.** There are easy, unprocessed foods recipes that you can quickly and easily throw together for your own, your significant other, or your entire family - and feel *good* about what you're serving to the people you love (you included!) Toward the end, you'll find a lot of information about supplements, the debate about dairy free milk... basically all frequently asked questions I get when people find out I'm a registered nutritionist. That being said, if you have any questions about something you read, or want to know more, **PLEASE do not hesitate to reach out**!

Most of these recipes are vegetable-centered and do not rely on animal protein. Personally, I find that I am my strongest and clearest when existing on a diet that doesn't include animal protein. With that said, I definitely don't label myself vegan or vegetarian. (Labeling the way you eat is a little too high stakes for my taste)! **I listen to my body every chance I get and really try to tune in to why I'm craving a certain food group**. I encourage you to try to do the same! And remember – I am NO perfect chef. I think these recipes are PERFECT for MY tastebuds, but feel free to shoosh them up! Add less sweetener if you're over sweets for a while, double the amount of chickpeas if you started your day with a ten-mile hike. Let these recipes be a starting point for you as you learn to consume more whole, **unprocessed foods**.

So much of what we consume should also be centered around the amount of activity we have in a day, the amount of stress we're under, our relationships with those we usually dine with, etc., so if you're looking for a specific 28-day meal plan, using recipes from this book, that will correlate with your daily habits, reach out to me and we'll get you started! Just like our bodies take in nutrients differently, we all respond differently to big mental-life changes. **I'm happy to walk alongside you on this journey to health and show just how accessible I believe healthy eating can be.**

THANK YOU for checking out this cookbook. THANK YOU for trusting me to hang out with you as you're recreating what the word "health" means to you. This passion of mine is something that has kept me sane and centered when everything else has felt out of control, so getting to share it with others is the greatest gift I can imagine. Let's work together and remember to keep it, **Low stakes baby!**

I Get by With a Little Help From My Friends

Personally, I love Holistic Nutrition because it's the study of food and how real, unprocessed, clean food can fuel us to be the best version of ourselves. If we're investing time in our own bodies, and finding the foods that make us feel good, we're more likely to "pour from a full glass" and invest in the people and relationships around us.

Growing up, my parents' favorite phrase was **"The richest crust is the crust that's shared."**

While I definitely take that literally to this day (catch me splitting a pb and j with anyone that will accept it!), I also think this phrase translates to a more ethereal concept. Some of my all-time favorite recipes were created after a conversation with a friend. I love nothing more than splitting a slice of avocado toast with a gal pal and deeply dissecting what other toppings could have been added. I love food because it brings people together and encourages us to raise the stakes when it matters, and keep them low when it doesn't!

Throughout these pages, I've mentioned friends that have inspired me through my nutritional journey up until now. I've also asked friends that excel in certain aspects of food prep or recipes to chime in on their areas of expertise. I hope these mentions and interludes can help bring us all a little closer and I hope you feel like you've gained a cookbook with some great recipes as well as some new holistic health-loving friends - a reminder that no one is alone on this journey to overall wellness!

Table of Contents

Sauces, Snacks, and Sides, Oh MY! 59

Sweet Treats 79

Smoothies

I am the smoothie's biggest fan. I love that it feels like a dessert for breakfast. I have completed MANY workouts dreaming about my mint-chip-post-run smoothie. I'll admit it, many studies have shown that your satiation factor is much higher when you physically chew and swallow your food. For that reason, I love to turn my smoothie into a smoothie bowl and top it with whatever my body is craving – more fruit, cacao nibs, hemp seeds, coconut flakes, honey, my homemade granola (keep scrolling for the recipe!) - the world is your oyster! This helps move the smoothie from a meal that's swallowed in seconds to a meal you can really sit and enjoy. However, if you're in a rush (or just craving an old-fashioned smoothie!) then make sure it is filled with high fiber fruits and veggies that will fuel you in your day!

The Best Green Smoothie

- 1 cup peeled and chopped cucumber (1 medium cucumber)
- 1 cup non-dairy milk of choice (Almond is my go-to!)
- 1 cup baby spinach
- ½ banana, peeled
- ½ cup frozen mango
- 2 Tablespoons hemp hearts (buy these in most natural foods stores)
- 1 Tablespoon ground flax seeds

Combine in a blender until smooth. (The mango will cut the green I promise!)

Sarah's Thoughts: If there's a fruit calling to you, follow your gut! I tend to follow this basic outline for smoothies with 1 cup of non-dairy milk, 1 cup of fresh or frozen fruit, some hemp hearts and flax seeds, and a cup of veggies! You'll see that most of my smoothie recipes follow this general formula, but don't be afraid to really make it hearty.

Pumpkin Pie Smoothie

- ½ frozen banana
- 1 cup frozen butternut squash
- 1 teaspoon maple syrup
- 1 Tablespoon almond/peanut butter
- 1 cup of non-dairy milk (I like oat for this one because it makes it even creamier, but any non-dairy option will work)
- Sprinkle of cinnamon (approx. 1 teaspoon)
- Splash of nutmeg (approx. 1 teaspoon)
- Pinch of salt

Blend 'em up!

Sarah's Thoughts: I am OBSESSED with butternut squash in my smoothies. Seriously. I usually turn to this smoothie when I'm craving something sweet, and sometimes it's even *too* sweet with the maple syrup – follow your stomach here! You could even throw in a date for added sweetness instead of the maple syrup. I also love adding a tablespoon of cacao powder for a chocolate moment. Don't get stuck on the page – start to play with what smoothie combo YOU love!

Chocolate Cherry Milkshake

- ½ frozen banana
- 1 cup frozen cherries
- 1 Tablespoon cacao powder
- 1 cup milk of choice
- 1 Tablespoon cacao nibs

Blend and enjoy!

Sarah's Thoughts: I love how SIMPLE this smoothie is. Again, feel free to play around with ingredients to match your taste buds! And remember – taste buds can change DAILY, so try and tune into what your body is wanting! There's no right or wrong when it comes to a simple smoothie.

PB Powerhouse 2.0

- ½ cup blueberries
- ½ cup strawberries
- 1 Tablespoon Peanut Butter
- 1 Tablespoon non-dairy milk (I love oat for the creamy factor and the macro blend with the PB!)
- 1 cup riced cauliflower

Let it blend and throw in extra ice if necessary!

Sarah's Thoughts: My first survival job when I moved to NYC was blending smoothies at the Peloton cycling studio. The PB Powerhouse was without a DOUBT our best seller, so I had to pay homage to her here. I've updated the recipe to balance out the macros a bit more (the 1.0 PB Powerhouse held almost ½ cup of PB and a protein powder with more ingredients than should be legal...) but I think you'll love her just as much as the 23rd street OG Peloton riders do! It definitely has the PB&J vibe going for it!

Mint Chip Gift Smoothie

Mint Chip Gift

- ½ frozen banana
- 1 cup of non-dairy milk (almond is my go-to here!)
- 1 Tablespoon cacao nibs
- Fresh mint leaves (I LOVE fresh mint, so I tend to throw 8-10 leaves in there, but definitely soul search for how minty fresh you want to feel!)
- *If* you're going to use a *clean* protein powder, I really recommend using this recipe. (The mint hides the flavor of it!)

Hit that blend baby blend!

Sarah's Thoughts: I named this "Mint Chip Gift" smoothie for a REASON. I went through a phase where I would make it Every. Single. Day. I could be in the most horrible mood and one sip immediately turned my day around. I love how simple the ingredients are and how much it tastes like a literal milkshake. I find I'm usually full with just half a banana, but if you're starving, go for the full! You can also use a high-powered blender, quadruple the recipe, freeze it and serve it up as the famous "banana nice cream," that would ABSOLUTELY cost you $8.95 in ANY vegan restaurant and you'd probably post it on Instagram!

Pineapple Adventure

- 1 cup frozen pineapple
- ½ cup banana slices (any tropical fruit is fun here – I also love strawberries, mango, or papaya)
- Non-dairy milk (I love coconut milk here – canned, no sugar added, reduced fat)
- ½ cup plain Greek yogurt
- Optional adds: honey, sub any 100% fruit juice for the non-dairy milk (I recently tried guava and loved it!), you can ALWAYS add ground flax seeds for extra fiber

Blend that honey up and add ice cubs or water to reach desired consistency

Sarah's Thoughts: Are you a Disney Dole Whip person?? Get ya Mickey ears on because this will transport you to that weird line outside of the Tiki Room. It's fruity and the perfect level of sweet. As always, feel free to play around with the ingredients and see what flavors you love!

Breakfast

I cannot emphasize enough how important breakfast is for both your mind and your soul. There have been numerous studies about the importance of consuming some sort of fuel within 30 minutes of waking up – Personally, I think it's best to listen to your body and eat when you're hungry! That being said, if you're consuming balanced meals throughout the day, while you sleep at night your body will digest everything from the previous day and you should wake up ready for some fuel. I like to work out first thing in the morning, but I always make sure I eat at *least* a no-bake energy bite (recipe on page 91) or a piece of peanut butter toast before asking so much of my body. When you perform a fasted workout, your brain sets off the same stress receptors that encourage your body to hold onto weight – definitely not ideal! All that said, your Grandma was right – Breakfast really is the most important meal of the day. And hopefully, these low stakes recipes will help get you off on the right foot!

Can I Try Your Granola??

- 4 cups oats
- 1 ½ cups raw nuts or seeds (You can totally get creative here – almonds, pumpkin seeds, pecans, walnuts; I usually check my pantry and see what I can throw in there!)
- 1 teaspoon sea salt
- 1 teaspoon cinnamon (You can cut this in half – I personally love cinnamon and don't think you can have too much!)
- 1/3 cup melted coconut oil
- 2 Tablespoons Maple syrup (You can add more if you like a sweeter granola - Also feel free to substitute honey or agave.)
- 1 teaspoon vanilla extract
- Optional add ins: ground flax seeds, unsweetened coconut, chocolate chips, dried cranberries, Chia Seeds (All around 2 Tablespoons)

Preheat your over to 350 degrees and line a large baking sheet with parchment paper. In a large bowl, mix all ingredients together. Pour your granola onto your prepared pan and use and your spoon to flatten the mixture into an even layer. Bake for about 20 minutes, remove granola from oven and allow it to cool, untouched for at least 45 minutes. Once it has cooled, feel free to mix in additions like chocolate chips or dried berries. Store in an airtight container for up to 3 months!

Sarah's Thoughts: I am a granola FIEND. The recipe title is homage to my consistent request anywhere I go. Seriously, my favorite hobby is sampling granola from coffee shops (There's an infamous story where I was RAVING to the barista about their granola and he finally caved and admitted to me that it was actually Nature Valley…. my heart dropped.) ANYWAY, I love to top my smoothies with a little bit of granola for some bonus carbs, top my Greek yogurt with it, or use it as cereal with some almond milk. A word of warning: This granola is so good it's easy to not notice how much you consume. A serving size is 1/3 of a cup, and while the chia and nuts help add punches of omega-3s and antioxidants, remember, more is not *always* better. Eat until you're full

Whole Wheat Blueberry Pancakes

(Makes 4 Servings)

- 1 cup whole wheat flower
- ½ cup whole wheat pastry flower (I like to add this to give the consistency a lighter feel, but feel free to sub in an extra ½ cup of regular wheat flour)
- 2 teaspoons baking powder
- 1 teaspoon ground cinnamon
- ½ teaspoon sea salt
- 1 cup plain almond milk
- 1/2 cup unsweetened apple sauce
- 1 teaspoon vanilla extract
- 1 ¼ cups fresh blueberries

In a large bowl, whisk flour, baking powder, cinnamon and salt. In a separate medium bowl, whisk almond milk, ¼ to ½ cup water (or additional almond milk), applesauce, and vanilla until blended. Pour milk mixture into flour mixture and stir until evenly combined. Set batter aside to rest 10 minutes (batter will be very thick – I love these pancakes because they almost have a scone feel to them!).

Heat a cast-iron griddle or nonstick skillet over medium heat until hot, and spray griddle with coconut oil. Stir blueberries into batter. Ladle about ¼cup batter onto the griddle and cook about 2 minutes or until bottoms are golden. Flip and cook 1 to 2 minutes longer, until pancakes are cooked through.

Sarah's thoughts: One of the greatest joys in my life is when I freeze these, forget they're in my freezer, and then FIND THEM. I love to top them with a bit of Greek yogurt and berries for added protein and even some honey if I'm feeling a sweet tooth. (pro-tip: microwave frozen berries for 45 seconds and you have a "berry compote" that will make you smile the rest of the day). These are definitely great pre work-out and will keep you full all morning long. The servings here feel large because the whole wheat flour is so filling, so don't be afraid to listen to your stomach! And know that your batter will definitely be thick. Cook it like a regular pancake, but feel free to flatten them a bit after your first flip. And feel free to mix up the mix-in! I've tried strawberries, bananas, slivered almonds – all bets are off baby!

Three Ingredient Pancakes

- 1/3 cup oats (I find rolled to be best)
- 2 eggs
- ½ banana
- ½ teaspoon baking powder (optional, but it'll give you a fluffier pancake!)
- OPTIONAL: a dash of cinnamon (personally, I like several dashes), a scoop of protein powder, berries or banana

Throw your ingredients into your magic bullet or blender and mix until you have your desired consistency. (The batter will be much thinner than the whole wheat pancakes)! Pour batter into your preheated and coconut oil sprayed pan. This recipe will make 3 large, hearty pancakes!

Sarah's Thoughts: Same rules apply here as with the whole wheat pancakes – play around with the recipe and your tastebuds! I love topping these with Greek yogurt and berries as well, but the eggs already serve up a healthy dose of protein, so no worries about the satiety factor. I also love to top my pancakes with honey, agave, or real maple syrup for an extra punch of sweet. Pancakes get a bad rap for being sugar and carb bombs because of the way they are served in restaurants, but these recipes prove they can also be part of a whole foods diet.

Peter's Sweet Potato Hash

- 1 Tablespoon of olive oil
- 2 cloves of garlic
- ½ white onion
- 1 cup sweet potato (diced in 1-inch cubes)
- 1 cup kale, sliced into ribbons
- Salt/Pepper to taste
- Red pepper flakes

In a large sauté pan over medium/high heat, add olive oil, onions and garlic. Sauté 3-4 minutes, until onions are softening. Add prepped potatoes, salt, red pepper flakes, and sauté 5-7 minutes. When potatoes are fork tender, add kale, stir, and let wilt for 1-2 minutes. Top with an egg and enjoy!!

- Hot Tips:
    - **Potato:** Prep your tato for the week with no seasoning. Cut em up, throw em in oven at 400 for 40 mins or until slightly crisped/desired char lol. (I like a little crunch.) If you prep, you don't have to wait for them in the pan – you can throw them in at the last minute to warm them!
    - **Kale:** leave stems on your kale! Crunchy amongst a sea of mush (if you're not using kale, add fresh spinach near the end for some yummy greenery, but just so the leaves wilt a tiny bit).
    - **Cherry/grape tomatoes:** Fresh! Feckin yum lil S and P on those lil guys and slap 'em on top -you have a nice POP o' flavor.

Peter's Thoughts: I think of this recipe as a true kitchen sink moment. Find what you have in the fridge and throw it in a pan before slappin' two eggs on top and calling it breakfast. This recipe starts with basic ingredients but LET'S GET CRAFTY. My favorite thing is adding bell peppers to the mix with the onions and garlic at the beginning. This WILL send your nostrils into a tailspin of delight. Then you come in with a dash of cumin, chili pow, salt and pepper, maybe if you feel hungry and only have one egg - but you want an extra boost, add black beans. A nice clean southern breakfast. You have asparagus and cherry tomatoes? Toss those in and add a sprinkle of goat cheese. Chef's kiss hennies. Mushrooms and a cut up slice if turkey bacon... mountain scramble. The possibilities are endless! I quite literally dare you to try something new every time you make a hash.

Tempeh Bacon

Tempeh Bacon

- For the Marinade:
    - 1 Tablespoon Tamari
    - 1 Tablespoon olive oil
    - 1 Tablespoon Maple Syrup
    - ½ teaspoon paprika
    - 2 teaspoon liquid smoke
    - ½ teaspoon cumin
- 8 ounces Tempeh (my favorite is the Trader Joe's Brand!)
- Olive oil Spray
- A bit of salt and pepper

Mix the marinade in a shallow bowl. Slice the tempeh as thin as you can (without letting it fall apart!) to recreate the look of bacon. Pour the marinade over the tempeh and let it absorb for 1 minute while heating your large, olive oil sprayed pan. Add the slices to the pan and cook approx. 1-2 min on each side. Salt and Pepper to your taste! Serve immediately, but your leftovers will last in an air tight container for up to a week.

Sarah's Thoughts: Full disclosure: I have never eaten pork bacon. HOWEVER, I fully believe that I never *need* to because this tempeh bacon is just so good! If you're watching your soy intake, it's also possible to create this exact recipe but using seitan. And the best part? It cooks up quicker than regular pork bacon!

Tofu-d Scramble

- 1 spray of olive oil
- 1 16-ounce block of tofu
- 2 Tablespoons nutritional yeast
- ½ teaspoon salt
- ¼ teaspoon turmeric
- ¼ teaspoon garlic powder
- 2 Tablespoons almond milk (any non-dairy will work – but definitely go unsweetened!)
- Optional: Additional veggies such as spinach, kale, red pepper. Chives for topping

Spray the bottom of a large sauce pan with olive oil and add your tofu block. Immediately mash the tofu using a fork or even a potato masher. Cook for around 4 minutes until the water from the tofu has evaporated. Add in your spices and stir for about 3 min. Finally stir in the non-dairy milk to your liking. Serve immediately (this recipe will feed 2 very hungry people!) Feel free to mix in the veggie of your choice - Don't forget to add chives on top for added bite!

Sarah's thoughts: This is another breakfast that is *almost* better the second day (I'm pretty sure it's because you get to look forward to having it again for 24 hours.) The nutritional yeast adds even MORE protein to the dish so coupled with the tofu – you'll be ready to literally lift up cars. I love this dish when I'm looking for a break from the classic egg scramble and always try to get really crafty with my toppings!

Yogurt Bowl

- ¾ cup Fage 0% or 2% unsweetened yogurt
- Possible toppings:
    - Cup of Berries
    - Any seasonal fruit (Check out the seasonal fruit list on page 124)
    - Granola
    - Hemp seeds
    - Coconut
    - Ground Flax seed
    - Honey
    - Cacao Power

Place ¾ cup Fage Greek yogurt in a bowl and top with toppings of your choice!

Sarah's Thoughts: If ANYONE reading this has a connection to Fage Yogurt, PLEASE let me know immediately – I'd like to send them a love letter. Fage is not only the cleanest Greek yogurt on the market, but I *personally* think it also holds the best flavor. You won't find a creamier Greek yogurt with a lower level of added sugars. It provides the perfect base for any toppings that call to you, so there's no limit to possible flavors in this bowl. Of course, we'll ideally keep dairy intake to a minimum on a day to day basis, but I find that this bowl is perfect when I'm craving something sweet first thing in the morning or even late at night as an after dinner treat that will keep me full all night long.

Protein-cado

Protein-cado

- Avocado (Half or Whole)
- 2 Tablespoons Nutritional Yeast
- Himalayan Sea Salt
- Olive Oil

Basically, cut your avocado in half and top with nutritional yeast, salt, and drizzle a small amount of olive oil for flavor.

Sarah's Thoughts: I love this dish purely for simplicity. I think the total time it takes from refrigerator to plate is 1 min and 36 seconds. It's perfect for mornings where you're tempted to stop and grab a high-sodium breakfast sandwich. It'll keep you full for HOURS and if you weren't already sold on nutritional yeast, remember that it contains thiamine, riboflavin, niacin, vitamin B6 and vitamin B12 – which ALL have been proven to increase serotonin levels. Besides, who doesn't get at least a little giddy when they cut open the perfect avocado?!

Overnight Oats

Things you NEED

- ½ cup rolled oats
- 3/4 cup almond milk

Things that are nice to add:

- ½ teaspoon chia seeds
- ½ cup greek yogurt
- Maple syrup
- Honey
- Fruit of choice (I love berries!)
- Coconut flakes
- Hemp seeds
- Cacao nibs

Put oats and milk in an airtight container (I love mini mason jars because they're easy to grab on the go!) and let them sit in the fridge overnight – or at least 8 hours. Add toppings when you're ready!

Sarah's Thoughts: Overnight oats are my absolute go-to when I am on the move and need something that will fully fuel me while still keeping me satisfied. You literally need only 2 ingredients to make them – anything else is icing on the cake. Personally, I usually mix in some Greek yogurt, chia seeds, and whatever fruit I have nearby. This tends to be my breakfast of choice when I'm traveling – You can always keep a bag of oats in your suitcase and ask Starbucks for a cup of almond milk if you're REALLY desperate (been there, done THAT.) Adding nut butter or a couple of raw nuts will also help your body slow down the process of carbs burning, and keep you fuller longer.

Lower the Stakes Avocado Toast and Tempeh Bacon

Lower the Stakes Avocado Toast

- Whole grain toast
- Avocado
- Squeeze of fresh lemon

Use 1/2 an Avocado and mash it in a bowl. Add a squeeze of (ideally) fresh lemon juice. Mash on your toast and enjoy!

Sarah's Thoughts: There is a SIMPLE reason avocado toast got bougie – It's. So. Good?! The healthy fats from the avocado balance out the carbs in the bread and it's an absolute treat. Don't get intimidated not to throw together an avocado toast for breakfast because that classy cafe decided to start charging $17 for it – you can make a PERFECT 'cado toast at home. I love to grab a homemade whole wheat bread from the farmers market, add "Everything but the Bagel" seasoning, and sliced mini tomatoes for the perfect morning fuel.

A Tip on Selecting a Whole Wheat Bread: When you check the nutrition facts label on a loaf of bread, check and see if the ratio of grams of carbohydrates to grams of dietary fiber is five or less. Also try to make sure that the first ingredient listed is *whole* wheat flour. This will help ensure that your body is getting the most bang for its buck calories wise and that you are consuming whole, intact grains whenever possible.

Lunch and Dinner

There's a reason that people gather around the table to dine with their family and friends for lunch and dinner. Lunch is a mid-day moment to assess our hunger level and our activity level for the rest of the day. Dinner is a chance to regroup and re-feed our muscles and souls after they've served us for at *least* twelve hours! These meals should satiate both your appetite and your eyes. Of course, it's vital that they include healthy fats, protein, and usually carbohydrates. I love lunch and dinner because these recipes make it so easy to create a dish for a full family and let everyone serve themselves what they want. Enjoy your lunch and your dinner, and don't be afraid to double recipes so you'll have grab-and-eat leftovers!!

Simple Taco Bowls

Makes 4 servings

- 2 cups fresh or thawed frozen corn off the cob
- ½ teaspoon ground cumin
- 1 teaspoon chili powder
- 1 teaspoon onion granules
- 3 cups black beans, cooked fresh
- 3 cups short-grain brown rice, cooked
- ½ head romaine lettuce, shredded
- 1 cup pico (can be purchased fresh)
- Avocado Jalapeño Crème for topping (See page 63)
- ½ cup dry toasted pumpkin seeds
- Hot sauce (optional)
- Whole wheat or corn tortillas, warmed (optional)

Preheat oven to 400°F. In a small bowl, add the freshly shucked or thawed corn. Mix with the cumin, chili powder, and onion granules. Spray a baking sheet or line with parchment paper and spread corn evenly. Roast 5 minutes. Remove and allow to cool. Set aside.

To assemble the bowls: Evenly distribute the beans, rice, roasted corn, and lettuce in each bowl. Top each bowl with Red Pepper Pico and Avocado-Jalapeno Crème, and garnish with pumpkin seeds. Serve with your favorite hot sauce, if you like, and warmed tortillas to assemble your own tacos.

Sarah's Thoughts: It doesn't get better than these bowls. They are customizable to ANY palette and they're sure to be a huge hit at any family gathering. Step aside Chipotle... there's a new gal in town!!

Penne Puttanesca with Roasted Red Pepper Sauce

Makes 4-6 servings

- 8 ounces whole wheat penne
- 1 cup small-diced white onion
- Crushed red chili flakes to taste
- 3 cloves garlic, minced
- ½ cup low-sodium vegetable broth
- 3 ½ chopped roasted red bell peppers
- ¼ cup pine nuts, dry toasted
- 1 Tablespoon balsamic vinegar
- ¼ teaspoon crushed red chili flakes
- 3 Tablespoons pitted and chopped kalamata olives
- ¼ cup chopped fresh parsley
- 3 Tablespoons fresh basil

Bring a large pot of water to boil for the pasta. Pour in the pasta, stir frequently, and cook until tender. Strain.

Place sauté pan on medium to high heat. When pan is heated, add the onion and sauté, stirring frequently until onion begins to stick. Add the chili flakes and garlic and cook for 2 minutes, stirring well. Add 2 to 3 tablespoons of vegetable broth to deglaze the pan, and remove from heat.

In a blender, add the sautéed onion and garlic, remaining vegetable broth, roasted red peppers, pine nuts, and balsamic vinegar; blend until smooth. Pour pepper puree into a medium saucepan over medium-low heat and slowly bring to a simmer, stirring frequently. Add crushed red chili, olives, parsley, and basil. Stir well and remove from heat. Add in the cooked penne and fold to coat pasta well. Serve immediately.

Sarah's Thoughts: When I am craving pasta, this is the only recipe that will do. I'm instantly transported to a fancy-glam restaurant in Manhattan and everyone around me has food envy of what I've ordered. It's a simple and pairs perfectly with a side of green vegetables. You can also add a protein to the dish if you're craving some macro balance here. And of course, feel free to get crafty and clever with your pasta shape choices!

Grandma's Quinoa Casserole

Grandma's Quinoa Casserole

- 1 cup quinoa
- 1 cup brown lentils
- 2 medium red potatoes
- 2 carrots (chopped into rings)
- 2 onions, chopped
- 2 cups vegetable stock
- 1 teaspoon chili powder
- ½ teaspoon cumin
- 1 ½ teaspoon tamari

Place quinoa in a bowl and cover with water. Swirl bowl and drain with a coriander. Repeat until the water runs clear. Place quinoa and other ingredients in a large pot and bring to a boil. Reduce heat and simmer until carrots are tender (about 30 min) Stir several times during cooking adding more vegetable stock if necessary. This will make 4 servings.

Sarah's Thoughts: I love how simple, easy, and customizable this dish is! I think quinoa gets a bad name sometimes because it takes a bit of effort to make. However, this is literally a drop and heat recipe so it's little work for you, high on flavor, and quinoa is gluten free and one of the few plant proteins that contains all 9 essential amino acids! I lovingly named it "Grandma's Quinoa Casserole" because it has the vibe of a comfort food meal that is ALSO a perfect treat to bring to a neighbor (Does that only happen in TV shows)? Feel free to play around with the added vegetables and see what works best for your taste-buds!

Spaghetti Squash with Pesto

- ½ cooked spaghetti squash
- 2 heaping cups of fresh basil
- 1 clove garlic
- 1/3 cup unsalted pumpkin seeds
- Juice from ½ lemon
- 2 Tablespoons olive oil
- ¼ teaspoon salt
- Optional: sprinkle of goat cheese

Preheat your oven to 425. Cut your spaghetti squash in half, lengthwise, and scoop out the seeds. Place cut-side down on a baking sheet and bake for about 35 minutes, until a fork can easily be inserted into the skin of the squash. Remove from the oven and scrape along the inside of the squash with a fork to reveal the "spaghetti". Meanwhile, add all pesto ingredients to a food processor or high-speed blender and whiz to combine. Toss spaghetti squash with pesto and top with optional sprinkle of goat cheese

Sarah's Thoughts: What do you think it was like for the first person who cut into a spaghetti squash?? How high did their heart soar when they discovered just how insanely tasty it is AND how much fun it is to make and eat?! I have made this pesto upwards of 15 different ways and it is literally foolproof. I've substituted basil for dandelion greens, the pumpkin seeds for cashews, and the olive oil for ghee. The list goes on and on, but hear me when I tell you that it is physically impossible for this dish to fall flat!

Turkey Burgers (Mediterranean)

- 1½ lbs. 93% lean ground turkey
- 1 medium red onion thinly slice half, finely chop half, divided use
- ¼ cup finely chopped sun-dried tomatoes
- 2 oz. frozen spinach thawed, squeeze out liquid using a kitchen towel, chopped
- 6 Tablespoons crumbled feta cheese
- 1 teaspoon dried oregano
- ½ cup whole grain bread crumbs
- 1 large egg
- Sea salt and ground black pepper to taste
- 1 medium cooked beet sliced thin (I like to buy prepackaged beets and slice and grill them!)
- ¼ medium cucumber sliced thin

Preheat grill or broiler to high. Combine turkey, chopped onion, sun-dried tomatoes, spinach, cheese, remaining 1 clove garlic, oregano, bread crumbs, and egg in a medium bowl. Season with salt and pepper if desired; mix well with clean hands. Form turkey mixture evenly into six patties. Grill or broil patties for about 5 minutes on each side, or until no longer pink in the middle. Serve patties topped evenly with yogurt sauce, onion slices, beet, and cucumber.

Sarah's Thoughts: Mediterranean is hands down my favorite cuisine. I love the flavors, the brilliant use of herbs and spices and the way they all combine to make a melody for your taste-buds. This dish is perfect when you're jonesing for a hit of flavor with your burger that won't leave you laying on the couch for the rest of the evening!

38   Turmeric Cauliflower Steak with No-Oil Hummus

Turmeric Cauliflower Steaks

- Head of Cauliflower
- 1 Tablespoon turmeric powder
- 1 Tablespoon olive oil
- ½ teaspoon black pepper
- ½ teaspoon garlic powder
- ½ teaspoon paprika
- Salt and Pepper to taste

Adjust your over rack to the bottom 1/3 of the oven and preheat to 500 degrees. Remove the outer leaves from the cauliflower and using a large knife, cut a 1 ½ inch steak out of the head – You should have around 4 "steaks." Drizzle olive oil on both sides of cauliflower and evenly sprinkle seasoning on each side as well. Tightly cover the baking sheet with foil and cook for 5 min. Remove the foil and roast for 10 min. Flip the steak and cook for an additional 6 min, or until steak is golden and crispy. Garnish to your liking!

Sarah's Thoughts: Okay, I have a friend who has a HUGE issue with "vegetables cosplaying as other things." And ever since she said that to me... I can't look at "cauliflower steaks" the same. That being said, this dish is so insanely filling and tasty, you won't regret trying it. The turmeric in this dish is honestly the unsung hero – reminder that turmeric is great for inflammation. Check out the other benefits of turmeric on page 122. I love to drizzle some maple dressing (page 69) or Avocado Jalapeño Crème (page 63) to give it an extra kick.

Cheesy Veggie Enchiladas

For enchilada sauce:

- 2 Tablespoons olive oil
- 2 Tablespoons flour
- 2 Tablespoons chili powder
- 1 can tomato sauce (8 oz)
- 2 cups water
- ½ teaspoon cumin
- ¼ teaspoon garlic powder
- ¼ teaspoon onion salt

Heat oil in a small sauce pan on medium heat. Stir in flour and chili powder and cook until lightly brown, stirring constantly. Stir in remaining ingredients until smooth and continue cooking over medium heat, approximately 10 minutes or until slightly thickened. I usually make this sauce first and let it simmer while I'm preparing the rest

For the enchiladas:

- 1 Tablespoon olive oil
- 1 cup chopped onion
- 1 red bell pepper
- 1 orange bell pepper
- 1 cup chopped zucchini
- 1 chopped poblano pepper
- 2 cups spinach
- 1 teaspoon each of: chili powder, onion powder, garlic powder, oregano, sea salt, cumin, and pepper
- ¼ cup plain Greek yogurt
- 1 ½ cups Monterrey Jack cheese
- 12 corn tortillas
- Pot of Enchilada sauce (above)

Preheat the oven to 350 degrees and spray a large baking dish. In a skillet, combine all your vegetables as well as chili powder, onion powder, garlic powder, oregano, sea salt, cumin, and pepper. In a small sauce pot, over very low heat, combine Greek yogurt, cottage cheese, and 1/3 cup Monterrey jack cheese. Stir until cheese melts and then pour cheese mixture in with veggie mix. Allow flavors to marinate and heat for 5 min. In each tortilla, place a spoonful of the mixture, roll tortilla and place in greased pan. Repeat with all tortillas. Pour enchilada sauce to cover enchiladas, top with remaining Monterrey Jack cheese, and bake for 30 minutes.

<u>Sarah's Thoughts:</u> Enchiladas from a restaurant, without FAIL, give me a stomach ache. I think it's the mix of the sodium with the unidentified oils, but the minute of satisfaction just isn't worth the way I feel the rest of the day. These are the perfect blend of hearty and light, and just cheesy enough to give flavor without threat of a stomach ache. I love swapping out the veggies because this recipe seriously cannot go wrong! This recipe makes a large portion and they reheat beautifully.

Sweet Potato Caesar Salad

- 1 serving of my Hail (Vegan) Caesar Dressing (page 60)
- 2 sweet potatoes
- 1 can of chickpeas
- 2 Tablespoons olive oil
- 1 teaspoon garlic powder
- ½ teaspoon onion powder
- ½ teaspoon paprika
- ¼ teaspoon cayenne
- 4 cups kale (I like to massage mine with a bit of olive oil before creating my salad)
- ½ avocado
- Salt and pepper to taste

Set oven to 425. Blend up a serving of Hail (Vegan) Caesar Dressing. Cube your 2 sweet potatoes and coat them with 1 Tablespoon olive oil, salt, and pepper. Bake at 425 for 30 min. Drain, rinse, and pat dry can of chickpeas. Toss them with 1 Tablespoon olive oil and other listed spices. Roll onto cooking tray lined with parchment paper and bake at 425 for 15 min.

Add kale, sweet potatoes, chickpeas, and avocado to a large bowl and toss with dressing. YUM.

Sarah's Thoughts: Since creating this recipe, it has become a staple in my everyday life. You have the protein punch of the garbanzo beans and the sweet/savory mix of the sweet potatoes and the dressing. The spices offer an antioxidant PUNCH so it's really a HUGE win for everyone involved. I mostly love that this can be both a side or a main dish!!

Hearts of Palm All-In-Pasta

Hearts of Palm All-In-Pasta

- 1 package of Hearts of Palm pasta (available at most organic grocers, and now Trader Joe's!)
- 1 cup kale
- 1 cup halved cherry tomatoes
- ½ cup sliced mushrooms
- 1 jar of tomato sauce (8 oz)
- 2 cloves garlic
- 1 Tablespoon goat cheese for topping
- 1 Tablespoon olive oil

Put 1 Tablespoon olive oil into a large sauté pan. Cook the kale for approx. 3 min, allowing it to soften. Add mushrooms, tomatoes, cherry tomatoes, garlic (and any other veggies or protein you may be interested in!). Let heat for 5 min until veggies just start to brown. Add your pasta and tomato sauce. Allow your dish to simmer, covered, for up to 20 minutes. Feel free to add salt and pepper for taste!

Sarah's Thoughts: Okay, this recipe came about from one of those "I have NOTHING to eat in this pantry" moments. I ended up throwing together what's come to be one of my all-time favorite dishes. This is a filling lunch or dinner, and definitely a volume meal. The kale even gives it a bit of crunch – grab a slice of whole grain garlic bread and you're suddenly in Italy!

Better Than Marie's Veggie Pot Pie

For Filling
- 1 Tablespoon olive oil
- 1 cup sliced or chopped mushrooms
- 1 cup chopped yellow onions
- 1 cup chopped zucchini
- 1 cup diced carrots
- ½ cup diced celery
- 1 ½ teaspoon garlic powder
- ½ teaspoon salt
- ¼ teaspoon pepper
- ¼ cup all-purpose flour
- 2 cups unsweetened almond milk
- ½ cup frozen peas
- 1 Tablespoon fresh thyme
- 1 egg

For Crust:
- 1 ¾ cup whole wheat flour
- 1 teaspoon salt
- ½ cup coconut oil
- 3 Tablespoons water

For Crust: Combine all crust ingredients except water. Add 1 Tablespoon at a time until dough is not sticky. Roll ½ of the dough between 2 pieces of waxed paper to desired size.

Preheat the oven to 425 degrees. Lightly coat a pie dish with coconut oil spray. Heat a large pan with 1 Tablespoon olive oil. Add mushrooms and onions and cook until they are beginning to brown. Add carrots, celery, zucchini, peas, thyme garlic powder, salt, and pepper. Cook approximately 5 minutes. Sprinkle the flour over the top of the vegetables and sit for 2 min. Slowly add 2 cups of almond milk and let simmer for approximately 10 min. Pour the mixture into your greased pie tin. Place crust over pot pie filling and mold crust to pan. Cover crust with a thin egg wash and bake for 25 min.

Sarah's Thoughts: I grew up with parents who LOVED Marie Calendar's frozen chicken pot pies. Personally, something was always missing for me. I think it was the sauce that seemed to take over the flavor of every vegetable. I love this recipe because it's simple and quick, yet still the ultimate comfort food. This crust recipe is my grandma's crust recipe and fair warning – while it's not always the prettiest (it can be a little crumbly sometimes...) the flakiness of it makes up for appearance ten-fold.

Lentil Soup

- 1 chopped yellow onion
- ¼ cup olive oil
- 2 diced carrots
- 2 sliced stalks of celery
- 2 minced cloves of garlic
- 1 teaspoon dried oregano
- 1 bay leaf
- 1 teaspoon dried basil
- 1 can (8 oz) crushed tomatoes
- 2 cups dry lentils
- 8 cups water or vegetable stock
- ½ cup spinach
- 2 Tablespoons vinegar
- Salt and pepper to taste

In a large soup pot, heat oil over medium heat. Add onions, celery and carrots and cook until veggies are tender. Stir in garlic, bay leaf, oregano, and basil and cook for 2 minutes. Stir in lentils, water or veggie stalk, and tomatoes. Bring to a boil. Reduce heat to a simmer, cover and let cook for at least an hour. When ready to serve, stir in the spinach.

Sarah's Thoughts: Jokes aside, I spent my first year living in NY surviving off of Trader Joe's packaged lentil soup. While that sweet burgundy box still holds a special place in my heart, when I perfected this recipe, my world really opened up. The flavors are just fresher, the veggies have a welcome crunch, and seeing the herbs go into the pot make you confident that your body is getting all the nutrients it deserves from a dish! I'll sometimes top this soup with avocado if I'm craving some healthy fats!

All the Veggies Roast

All the Veggies Roast

- Veggies of your choice
- 1 Tablespoon Olive Oil

Lay veggies on a sheet pan. (Cover the pan in foil for easy clean up!) Drizzle with olive oil and bake at 400 degrees for 30-40 min. Stir vegetable mixture every 10 min.

Sarah's Thoughts: This recipe is honestly just a reminder of how EASY it to is create a nutritious side dish for ANY meal. Challenge yourself to buy one veggie you love and one you've never tried before at the farmer's market this week! After a lot of trial and error, I've personally discovered that my favorite vegetables to roast are butternut squash and red onion. As long as those two veggies are in the mix, I can add anything else for more nutrients and know that I'm going to love the taste. Don't give into the "I have to make a PERFECT dish" mentality – you never know what you might discover. Pro-tip: Google is your friend! Don't be afraid to search "How long should I roast Brussel sprouts SOS?!" This is a learning process – use your tools!

Stuffed Sweet Potato

Makes 4 Servings

- 4 medium sized sweet potatoes
- 1 teaspoon lime juice
- ½ teaspoon pepper
- ½ medium red onion
- ¼ teaspoon garlic powder
- ½ teaspoon onion powder
- ¼ teaspoon cumin
- ¼ teaspoon chili powder
- ½ teaspoon sea salt
- 1 can (8 oz) black beans – rinsed
- For serving: 2 Tablespoon Greek yogurt (optional for topping), 1 avocado, chopped fresh cilantro

Preheat oven to 350 degrees. Place sweet potatoes on a foil covered baking sheet and bake for approx. 50 minutes. When sweet potatoes are 10 minutes from finished, sauté the onions on medium heat. Add in spices and lime juice. When onions are tender, add the black beans for about 5 minutes, stirring frequently. Remove sweet potatoes from the oven and allow to cool. Slice the sweet potatoes open, add black bean mixture, and top with avocado, Greek yogurt, and fresh cilantro.

Sarah's Thoughts: These guys are perfect when you're craving that tex-mex flair! Personally, I get crafty with this guy, sometimes adding my Avocado Jalapeño Crème or pumpkin seeds on top for added omega-3s. I love sweet potatoes because of their gut health positive impact and their high levels of vitamin A. Stuffed sweet potatoes are a forgotten art – you could even try making a sweet version with peanut butter and bananas for a sweet/savory breakfast!

Smashed Bean Salad

- 1 ½ cups canned white beans
- 1 Tablespoon lemon juice
- 1 Tablespoon olive oil
- 1 garlic clove
- Handful of arugula, chopped (any salad green will do!)
- A few basil leaves
- ½ teaspoon paprika

Place all your ingredients in a food processer and pulse until your dish is chunky, but not smooth. Use it on toast, in a taco, or to top a salad!

Sarah's Thoughts: I spent a really long time thinking that beans *weren't* the greatest food group because they were "so full of carbs!" How wrong I was. Seriously, beans are one of the most magical food products on the planet. White beans are way up there on the list of low calorie, nutrient dense foods, they reduce cholesterol, decrease blood sugar, and are FULL of fiber so they leave you feeling FULL. What more can we ask for?! I love how simple this recipe is, but I'm always trying out different flavors depending on my mood – currently I love stirring in some mustard or apple cider vinegar. See what floats your boat!

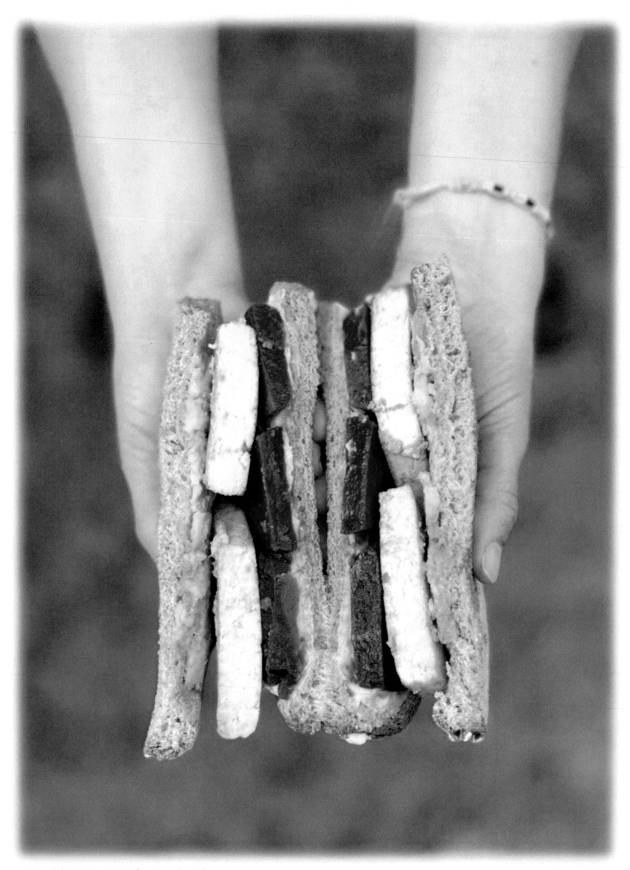

World Famous Tofu Sandwich

World Famous Tofu Sandwich

- 1 Tablespoon sesame oil
- 1 block tofu
- ½ sliced avocado
- ½ medium red onion (I like to use my marinated red onions on page 73)
- 3 slices of cucumber
- 2 Tablespoons no oil added hummus (page 61)
- 2 sliced beets
- 2 slices of whole wheat bread (Remember the 5 to 1 rule when selecting!)

Drain your tofu and cut into thirds, creating slabs. Heat oil in a pan over medium heat. Make crispy tofu by pan frying for about 2 min on each side. Toast your bread slices and assemble sandwich with tofu, mashed avocado, red onion (or my easy marinated onions on page 73), cucumber, hummus, and beets.

Sarah's Thoughts: This sandwich is, in my humble opinion, perfect. "World Famous" might be a stretch… but it's my cookbook baby and I'm creating the reality!! If I'm feeling really flirty, I'll add some dried oregano, mustard, or even a fried egg if I'm dying for protein on top of protein. You'll walk away from this sandwich feeling satisfied, and calling your best friend to tell them about it. (Step one towards ultimate world fame I tell ya….)

Mediterranean Chickpea Salad

Salad Ingredients:
- ½ chopped red onion
- 2 cans (8 oz) rinsed chickpeas
- 1 cup chopped parsley
- 1 sliced red bell pepper
- 1 sliced orange bell pepper
- ½ large cucumber
- ½ cup crumbled feta
- ½ cup halves kalamata olives

Dressing Ingredients:
- 3 Tablespoons olive oil
- 3 Tablespoons red wine vinegar
- 2 cloves minced garlic
- 1 ½ teaspoons dried oregano
- 1 teaspoon salt
- ½ teaspoon pepper

Place in onions in a bowl of water and let them soak to remove a bit of the harsh onion flavor (pro tip alert!). Place the chickpeas, parsley, bell peppers, cucumber, and feta in a large serving bowl. In a small measuring cup, stir together the dressing ingredients. Drain the onions and add them to the chickpea mixture, pour the dressing on top, and stir well. Refrigerate for 30 min to let the flavors marinate!

Sarah's Thoughts: There's a reason the Mediterranean fad diet was so popular – High nutrients and low calories make everybody happy. This salad is quick to put together, pleasing to the eyes, and the perfect side dish or main course for any get together. It doesn't get better than Mediterranean flair.

Mama Miyoshi's Teriyaki Chicken Wings

- 1 lb. chicken wings and drumsticks
- ¾ cup cooking Sake
- ¾ cup Mirin
- ¾ cup Soy Sauce
- 1 Tablespoon Sesame Oil

Place the wings and drumsticks in a medium sized pot and fill it with water until it covers all of the chicken. Boil at high heat until the skin of the chicken turns white.

Once the chicken has been lightly cooked, empty the water and rinse the chicken to remove all of the scum that has floated to the top.

Return the chicken to the pot and add the cooking sake, mirin, soy sauce, and sesame oil, and bring to a subtle boil on medium-high heat.

As the mixture begins to boil, add the lid to your pot, allowing an inch of space for steam to escape, and periodically mix the chicken to ensure that each piece takes turns being submerged in the mixture.

Continue this for roughly 20-30 minutes, or until the mixture has cooked off and turned into the consistency of teriyaki sauce. Enjoy!

Delphi's Thoughts: Wings are a guilty pleasure snack for me and my mama's Japanese Teriyaki Wings have always been my favorite. As she taught me this recipe, she told me that she loves how clean and light they taste because of the first step; the boiling of the chicken in order to remove the not-so-healthy bits that we usually associate with wings. I've written this recipe to accommodate a pound of wings and drumsticks, but if you're like me and you know you won't be sharing with just a pound, then the magical Japanese trifecta of sake/miring/soy sauce should cover roughly ¾ of the desired amount of chicken. I hope you enjoy this easy and tasty recipe from my home!

Butternut Squash Ricotta Toast

Butternut Squash Ricotta Toast

- 2 cups diced butternut squash
- 1 cup diced apples
- 3 Tablespoons olive oil
- ½ teaspoon ground cinnamon
- ¼ teaspoon ground nutmeg
- ¼ teaspoon all spice
- ¼ teaspoon ground cloves
- 1 teaspoon salt
- 1 teaspoon black pepper
- 10 slices of whole wheat baguette
- ¾ cup skim ricotta cheese
- 4 cloves minced garlic
- 5 Fresh chopped sage leaves
- 2 Tablespoons balsamic reduction

Preheat the oven to 425 degrees. Toss the butternut squash and apples with 2 Tablespoons of olive oil, cinnamon, nutmeg, all spice, ground cloves, salt, and pepper. Place on an even layer on a baking sheet and cook for 15 min. Combine the Ricotta cheese with ½ teaspoon black pepper and ½ teaspoon salt. In a small skillet, heat 1 Tablespoon olive oil and lightly sauté garlic and sage leaves for about 2 minutes. Remove from heat and toss the sage with the roasted butternut and apples. Top your toast with the ricotta cheese mixture, a spoonful of squash, and a drizzle of balsamic reduction. Voila!

Sarah's Thoughts: Seriously, this dish is game-over for me. The flavors are unexpected, but perfect, and in my humble opinion, the garlic sage takes it to another level. (check out the benefits of sage on page 122) This is the perfect dish to serve as an appetizer, or use thick whole wheat slices instead of a baguette to serve up an open-faced sandwich style. The ricotta packs a protein punch, the bread provides whole grain, squash for veggies, and apples as a fruit – talk about a well-rounded meal.

Elise's Quick Bolognese

- ½ lb ground beef
- 1 teaspoon butter
- ¼ Zucchini chopped
- ¼ Onion chopped
- 3 Baby Bella Mushrooms
- ½ Russet Potato chopped
- ½ 2 Carrot chopped
- ¼ Bell pepper chopped
- 1 Tablespoon olive oil
- Parmigiana Reggiano
- Tomato sauce of choice

Heat teaspoon butter in a large pan on med-high heat, add ground beef and add any spices you desire (salt, garlic, oregano, etc.) Cook until you see no pink. Remove beef from pan and set aside, dump grease into trash while still leaving enough to coat the pan. Add tablespoon of olive oil and potatoes to the pan, cook at medium-high heat and with the lid on for 5 minutes. Add the rest of vegetables, a good pinch of salt and garlic powder and stir together. Cook for another 5 minutes (or until you feel everything is sautéed well). Place cooked vegetables and desired serving of ground beef in a bowl, top with tomato sauce (however much you want) and shredded Parmesan. Mix together and enjoy! While this recipe serves one, you can use leftover ground beef to make the same thing tomorrow!!

Elise's Thoughts: Hi friends!! Elise here, Sarah's BFF – bonded by a love of unprocessed foods. This is a simple, fast recipe that is warm and comforting like a true Bolognese (but would make my Nonna roll in her grave because I'm using jarred tomato sauce.) The KEY HERE is SOURCING. You want to make sure your ground beef and butter is grass fed, your tomato sauce is clean, vegetables organic and your Parmesan is Parmigiana Reggiano (The real deal parmesan cheese. Anything else is imitation.) If your ingredients are solid than this meal is nourishing in every way. Love your ingredients and they will love you back!! Enjoy!!

Mary Elizabeth's Ginger Soy Tilapia with Broccoli and Coconut Rice

Makes 4 Servings

- 4 pieces skinless tilapia
- 1 head of broccoli, cut into florets
- 4 Tablespoons of low sodium soy sauce (or coconut aminos)
- 4 Tablespoons melted coconut oil
- 2 cups of light coconut milk
- 1 cup rinsed basmati or jasmine rice
- 1 inch piece of fresh ginger (peeled and minced)
- 4 scallions chopped
- chili flakes (sprinkled to your desired spice)

Preheat oven to 400 degrees Fahrenheit. Cut parchment paper into 4 pieces that you will fold around your fish and broccoli.

Pour 2 cups of light coconut milk and 2 Tablespoons of water into a pot. Heat to a boil. While you wait for that pot to boil because everyone knows a watched pot never boils, assemble the packets of fish. Arrange equal portion of broccoli florets next to each piece of fish on top of each piece of parchment paper. Drizzle each serving with 1 Tablespoon of soy sauce and 1 Tablespoon of coconut oil. Top each with minced ginger, scallions, and your desired amount of chili flakes.

By now that coconut milk should be boiling, hallelujah! Add in 1 cup of rinsed rice and reduce heat to a simmer and cover. Rice will take about 15-20 minutes to cook. Stir every so often. Add water as needed if all liquid is gone, but rice is not tender.

While rice is cooking create a packet by folding the parchment paper up and around the fish then fold the three open sides to makes a bag. Place the packets on a baking sheet and bake for 15 minutes, until fish is opaque and flakes easily with fork.

Mary Elizabeth's Thoughts: This dish is so flavorful! It is honestly easy prep and minimal dishes, which is always a win! I have made it many times just for myself and done one piece of fish and a few broccoli florets. You can easily half the rice portion by doing 1 cup of coconut milk and 1/2 cup of rice.

Sauces, Snacks, and Sides, Oh MY!

Meals. Should. Taste. Good. It seems so obvious when you write it out – But I am constantly amazed by how many people seem to think that "eating in a way to fuel my body" means that you're constantly eating unseasoned chicken and never-ending stalks of boiled broccoli. I love dressings, sauces, and side dishes that pair perfectly with a main course because they elevate your dining experience. They are the added costumes and scenery to an already lovely performance. You mean you can throw any veggies from your fridge in a bowl and top it with one of my homemade dressings and suddenly you're dining in a swanky restaurant?! It's practically a magic trick! Like I've said before – eating is a shared experience. I love these upcoming recipes because they so easily upgrade simple recipes. And because they were created at a baseline level, you can feel free to add ingredients and season them to your liking! Try adding bell pepper or edamame to my no-oil-added hummus! Throw in some oregano and see what happens. I love to have Tupperware full of salad dressings and sauces to level-up a meal at any given moment. I also love that this section is easily shared – don't be afraid to bring a side of brussels and mushrooms to your family potluck. You never know who might find a previously unsung love for veggies because they're finally trying them with a balsamic glaze!!

Hail (Vegan) Caesar! Dressing

- 1 cup cashews
- 1 ¼ cup water
- 2 Tablespoons fresh lemon juice
- 2 Tablespoons capers
- 2 Tablespoons water from capers jar
- 2 Tablespoons Dijon mustard
- 2 Tablespoons vegan mayo
- 2 peeled garlic cloves
- 2 Tablespoons nutritional yeast
- Salt and pepper to taste

Soak your cashews for an hour. Drain the water, add all ingredients to a blender and give it a whirl!

Sarah's Thoughts: Okay, while my go-to is to use this on my sweet potato Caesar salad, it is a PERFECT dressing for just about any salad. Only have kale in the fridge? Go for it! Throw it on some romaine and croutons and you're in BUSINESS. I don't want to get TOO crazy, but it would also be delicious as a dip for a veggie platter – the possibilities are endless!

Simple No-Oil Hummus

Makes 6 Servings

- 1 can (8 oz) no-salt-added garbanzo beans, rinsed and drained
- 2 cloves garlic
- 3 Tablespoons lemon juice
- 2 Tablespoons tahini
- ½ teaspoon ground cumin
- ½ teaspoon reduced sodium tamari
- ¼ teaspoon ground coriander
- Cayenne for spice
- Optional: 2 Tablespoons finely chopped fresh parsley

Put garlic in a food processor and pulse to roughly chop. Add garbanzos, ¼ cup water, lemon juice, tahini, cumin, tamari, coriander, and a pinch of cayenne, and process until creamy and smooth. Transfer to a bowl, cover, and chill for at least 1 hour. Before serving, let hummus come to room temperature. Stir in parsley if you're feeling a little extra flirty!

Sarah's Thoughts: It just doesn't get better than homemade hummus. I love that this recipe doesn't use any added oil, and I love putting a scoop of it on my salad and then drizzling the salad with olive oil. Because there's no oil in the actual recipe, it leaves you with just the right consistency to avoid soggy lettuce (Frankly, my worst nightmare.) Feel free to experiment with flavors of this hummus as well – add some roasted red pepper, caramelized onions, the list is never-ending!

Avocado-Jalapeño Crème

Avocado-Jalapeño Crème

Makes 6 servings

- 2 avocados
- 2 cloves garlic
- 2 Tablespoons lime OR lemon juice
- 1 jalapeño, seeded
- ¼ cup cilantro, chopped
- ¼ cup almond or soy milk, unsweetened
- Sea salt to taste

Blend ingredients (I like to use my magic bullet!) until smooth.

Sarah's thoughts: Once you try the crème, you don't turn back. It's such a solid dip to have on hand at all times. It spiffs up any dish in seconds, and you hold the power to deciding just how much spice you'll add to your topping. The almond milk gives it a creamy consistency while allowing the sauce to remain dairy free, making it the perfect topping for your burrito bowls, your morning eggs, your overnight oats, anything! (Just kidding about the oats... wanted to make sure you're still paying attention!)

Clean Tzatziki Sauce

- ¾ cup reduced-fat (2%) Greek yogurt
- 2 Tablespoons fresh lemon juice
- 1 clove garlic, finely chopped
- ¼ teaspoon dried dill weed

Combine yogurt, lemon juice, garlic, and dill in a small bowl; mix well. Refrigerate, covered, until needed.

Sarah's Thoughts: I created this dip for the Mediterranean Turkey Burgers on page 37, but this sauce has taken on a life of its OWN. I love keeping it in the fridge to dip veggies, top my salad with it, or even put it on eggs in the morning. There's no end to the positive vibes from this sauce, and you can't beat how quick and easy it is to whip up! And it's just a bonus that "oh, I just whipped up a fresh batch of Tzatziki" is so fun to say.

Tangy Red Wine Vinaigrette

- 3 Tablespoons red wine vinegar
- 1 Tablespoon olive oil
- 2 Tablespoons shallots finely diced
- Salt to taste

Hand whisk with a fork and mix, mix, mix baby!

Sarah's Thoughts: I love this dressing when I'm crunched for time and throwing every vegetable in my fridge in a bowl. It compliments just about any flavor – olives, onions, bell pepper, cucumber, tomatoes, hearts of palm, you name it! So, when you're in the mood for a light salad and a dressing that won't overpower the flavors of the sweet, sweet veggies, make this your new go-to! I put it in a spritzer bottle and keep nearby for salads big and small!

The World's Easiest Jam

The World's Easiest Jam

- 4 cups frozen blueberries (fresh work too!!)
- ¼ cup water
- 2 Tablespoons honey or 100% pure maple syrup
- 2 Tablespoons fresh lemon juice
- 2 Tablespoons chia seeds

Add all the ingredients to a medium pot. Cook on medium high heat for about 30 min, stirring occasionally. Allow to cool. This will last about a week in the fridge!

Sarah's Thoughts: The best part of homemade jam is that ANYTHING goes. I've made jam with just about every fruit imaginable. Don't be afraid to experiment! When you cook fruit down, it only gets sweeter and sweeter, so make sure you play around with the amount of honey or maple syrup you add.

Maple Nectar Dressing

Maple Nectar Dressing

- 1 Tablespoon Tahini
- 2 Tablespoons Maple Syrup
- 1 Tablespoon lemon juice
- 2 Tablespoons apple cider vinegar
- 1 clove garlic
- Salt and pepper to taste
- Water for thinning

Whisk together ingredients (You can use a fork OR blend it for a super creamy consistency), Start with these ingredients as a base, and then begin whisking in up to 2 tablespoons of water until you reach a desired consistency. Use it as a salad dressing, on your sweet potato, ANYTHING.

Sarah's Thoughts: The first time I drizzled this dressing on my sweet potato, I thought I had died and gone to heaven. I'm not exaggerating – I asked my roommate to come home IMMEDIATELY so he could sample it and reassure me that I hasn't lost it completely. The Maple syrup blends perfectly with the apple cider vinegar to create a sweet and savory combo that is truly unparalleled. I love using it on salads that have a heartier taste to them – think kale and butternut squash topped with pumpkin seeds?!? I'm drooling.

Super Food Salad Dressing

- ½ cup lemon juice
- 1 teaspoon tarragon leaves
- ¼ teaspoon ground pepper
- 1 teaspoon honey
- ½ teaspoon Dijon mustard
- ½ cup flaxseed oil
- ½ cup sunflower oil
- ¼ cup toasted almonds

Place ground pepper, honey, mustard, almonds, and tarragon leaves, and lemon juice in a small bowl and mix well. Add oil slowly, mix continuously until dressing is a light creamy color. Refrigerate for an hour before serving. This will make at least 12 salads so seal in an air tight container and save for a rainy day!

Sarah's Thoughts: I think sometimes restaurants label things "superfoods" when they don't want to be bothered to list the actual health benefits, so we've become a bit numb to the term. At a core level, a superfood is "a nutrient dense food considered to be especially beneficial for health and well-being." While "superfood" has become a buzzword among holistic health-ers, it's actually very low stakes, and it doesn't get much better than this herb filled dressing. I've started making a giant mason jar of this dressing and then adding ingredients based on my mood. I love mixing in a shot of liquid smoke for a BBQ style salad. Or adding almond milk and leaving out the lemon if I'm craving a creamier style dressing. As ALWAYS, the world is your oyster, baby!

Red Cabbage Side Salad

- 1 medium head red cabbage, coarsely chopped
- 10 sliced radishes
- 3 diced apples
- 2 green onions, chopped
- 1 stalk of celery, chopped
- ¼ cup chopped walnuts
- 1-2 Tablespoons lemon juice
- 1 teaspoon garlic powder
- 2 Tablespoons Olive Oil
- 1 Tablespoon balsamic vinegar

Mix all ingredients in a bowl and let sit for an hour. Makes 4 servings.

Sarah's Thoughts: Did you know that red cabbage is praised for its high levels of vitamin K, fiber, magnesium, zinc, and calcium?! I don't know about you, but I tend to forget about my pal red cabbage. He's always there for me... but I don't always give him his due! The crunch in this recipe is unparalleled, and the flavor only gets better as it marinates in the fridge, so I recommend making it at the beginning of the week and having it in your fridge for those "I need a veggie in my body now but I also want FLAVOR" moments. (You guys have those too, right??)

Marinated Red Onions and Simple No-Oil Hummus

Marinated Red Onions

- ½ red onion (sliced *thin)*
- ¾ cup extra virgin olive oil
- 1 Tablespoon dried oregano
- 1 Tablespoon red wine vinegar
- 1 to 2 teaspoons balsamic vinegar

Thinly slice the red onion and place slices in a bowl. Mix in the remaining ingredients. Let the onions marinate for 12 hours – they will last uncovered on the counter for up to 3 days!

Sarah's Thoughts: In my house, we call these onions the magical potion. Seriously, there is NO dish that isn't improved by adding a spoonful of these guys. And the unheated olive oil has more health benefits than you ever thought possible. I'll add them to my avocado toast, use the onions and olive oil as a salad dressing, on a sandwich – the possibilities are endless! And if you don't LOVE the smell of marinating onions in your kitchen 24/7, feel free to cover your bowl with saran wrap!

Grilled Basil Pineapple

- ½ cored pineapple (cut into moons)
- ½ cup basil leaves
- 1 Tablespoon olive oil
- Salt and pepper to taste

Heat your grill to high. Place the pineapple on grill for about 2 minutes per side. Let the pineapple cool and toss with basil, olive oil, salt, and pepper. Serve immediately or chilled!

Sarah's Thoughts: This is hands DOWN my favorite side dish to bring to any barbecue. It immediately transports you to Hawaii, people are blown AWAY by the mix of pineapple and basil, and the health benefits are never ending. I also love that by grilling the pineapple and adding the olive oil at the end, you take away some of the acid in the pineapple that always leaves my tongue feeling swollen. This is a perfect dish for when you need a burst of natural sugar energy.

Mama Jacqui's Famous Ranch

- 1 cup vegan mayo (I like Primal Foods for their clean ingredients)
- 1 teaspoon lemon
- 2 teaspoons vinegar
- ¼ cup oat milk
- ½ teaspoon salt
- ½ teaspoon pepper
- 1 teaspoon parsley
- 1 Tablespoon chopped fresh basil

Blend using a magic bullet or regular sized blender and store in an airtight container. Adjust herbs to your taste.

Mama Jacqui's Thoughts: This ranch is the perfect addition to any spring salad. It's much lighter than any packaged version and is so quick and easy to whip up. I love using it as a dip for veggies for an early afternoon snack. It freshens any simple green medley and transports you back to childhood – It's a staple in our kitchen!

Balsamic Sprouts and Mushrooms

Balsamic Sprouts and Mushrooms

- 1 lb brussel sprouts
- 2 Tablespoons olive oil
- 1 Tablespoon balsamic vinegar
- Salt and pepper to taste

Preheat your oven to 425. Toss sprouts and mushrooms with olive oil, salt & pepper, and arrange in a single layer on a baking sheet. Bake for 10 minutes, toss, and bake another 10-12 minutes until golden. Remove from the oven, toss sprouts and mushrooms with balsamic, and sprinkle with a touch of pink Himalayan sea salt. This will serve 2 (or 1 if you're like me and can't stop yourself!)

Sarah's Thoughts: A super fun fact is that mushrooms are literally the most protein packed vegetable. I've been weird about mushrooms ever since Ryleigh E spilled the beans about the whole fungus thing on the playground in elementary school, BUT I can't deny their positive impact on the nutritional world. I've even come to love and crave their flavor. The earthy taste of the mushrooms, mixed with the brussels and the balsamic topping literally makes my mouth water.

Sweet Treats

Let's face it: Sweet treats are one of the greatest joys in life. My best friend used to say that when she met someone new, her first question would be "what're your opinions on dessert?" She used it as the ultimate litmus test for friendship, and honestly... I think she's on to something. Let's remember – sugar is physically addictive. They more you eat it, the more you crave it. That's why personally, I've worked to train my taste buds to crave whole, natural sugars instead of packaged, processed, refined sweets. The following recipes are perfect for indulging your sweet tooth (Side note: I HATE when people say "this will kick that sweet craving to the curb" – we don't need to *ignore* the craving for sugar, we just need to fuel ourselves with sugars that are usable and helpful to our bodies! By not making sugar EVIL we are setting ourselves up for success and establishing a "lifestyle" rather than a "diet" mentality.) I don't think there is a better sentence in the English language than "oh my gosh – TRY THIS" and it seems most used around the dessert table. Instead of giving up brownies altogether, I encourage you to try to replace them with my sweet potato brownies, so you're reaping some health benefits along with your sweet treat! And remember – we always reach for what we have on hand. Most of these treats are easily freeze-able, so don't be afraid to try out a bunch and freeze them for a rainy day!

Natural Choco-Sauce

- 4 Tablespoons coconut oil
- 4 Tablespoons honey
- ½ cup cacao powder

Melt coconut oil and whisk with cacao powder and honey. Use as a drizzle, dip or topping!

Sarah's Thoughts: Honestly, I probably should have put this recipe about 4 pages earlier in the dips and dressing section. There is NO dish that isn't improved by this sauce. It's not TOO sweet, but it adds that chocolate flavor we crave. Bonus: You don't have to worry about any processed additives in your store- bought chocolate bar. Remember, this isn't necessarily a nutrient dense indulgent, so let's not get CRAZY…… but it doesn't hurt to have a jar in the fridge… at all times.

Banana GF/Grain free/Sugar free/Dairy free/Everything But the Fun Free Muffins

- 1 cup creamy peanut butter
- 2 large, spotty bananas
- 2 Tablespoons honey
- ½ teaspoon vanilla
- ½ teaspoon baking powder
- ½ cup chocolate chips, blueberries, strawberries (any add in your desire!)

Preheat your oven to 400 degrees. Grease a muffin tin with coconut spray oil. Combine all your ingredients in a blender and pour batter into prepared muffin tin. Bake for 15-17 min!

Sarah's Thoughts: As you may have guessed, I love baking with peanut butter. I think it's such a great way to give into your sweet tooth while boosting your energy levels, reducing risk of heart disease, and reducing risk of colon cancer. During my "count every calorie you consume" phase of life, I convinced myself I didn't like peanut butter; I want to apologize to everyone who ever had to listen to me say that. How disrespectful to my main man, PB. I love the consistency of these muffins and the fact that they still rise even without the flour. You can play around with the mix-ins as well. These are my favorite late-night snack that keep me full all the way to morning!

Doesn't-Get-Simpler Peanut Butter Cookies

Doesn't-Get-Simpler Peanut Butter Cookies

- ½ cup organic coconut flour
- ½ cup peanut butter
- 2 Tablespoons Maple Syrup
- 1 teaspoon vanilla
- 1 teaspoon coconut oil
- Sea Salt to top (optional)
- Natural choco-sauce to drizzle – page 80 (optional)

Mix the peanut butter, maple syrup, and vanilla extract. Slowly start mixing in flour (I find a fork works best!) Once dough forms, roll the dough into equal sized balls, aiming for around 16 cookies. Use a fork to flatten cookies. I like to add some sea salt and drizzle some natural chocolate sauce over the top (Go OFF), and refrigerate for at least 30 minutes before consuming.

Sarah's Thoughts: These are my absolute go-to when I need to bring a sweet treat to a party and don't want to worry about crazy refined sugar treats! You definitely need to be a PB lover to love these cookies, but you can also substitute almond butter, mixed butter, and the list goes on! These are the perfect little something sweet when you're craving something before bed OR to have alongside a Greek yogurt bowl!

Chocolate Dipped Strawberries

Chocolate Dipped Strawberries

- Strawberries
- Natural Choco-sauce (page 80)
- Additional toppings (coconut flakes, maca powder, cacao nibs, etc.)

Dip your strawberries one by one in natural choco-sauce, dip in any additional toppings, and refrigerate for at least an hour. Yum!

Sarah's Thoughts: Honestly, I can't be left alone with these. I love adding additional dip ingredients to pack a bit of nutrition with my treat here. Maca powder has quickly become my favorite, as it gives the berry a subtle earthy undertone *and* maca has been proven to dramatically improv your mood due to pheromone increase. As always, too much of a good thing is... not a good thing any more. So, make sure to enjoy these babies in moderation!

Chocolate Chia Pudding

- 2 Tablespoons chia seeds
- 1 Tablespoon cacao powder
- Sprinkle of salt
- Sprinkle of cinnamon
- 1 Tablespoon honey
- ½ teaspoon vanilla extract
- ½ cup almond milk (any dairy free milk will work!)

In a bowl, whisk everything together: your cacao powder, honey, vanilla extract, dairy free milk, salt, cinnamon, and chia seeds. Leave the mixture in the bowl for 5 min without stirring. After 5 minutes, whisk the mixture again. Pour the mixture in a small bowl, cover, and refrigerate for at least 8 hours.

Sarah's Thoughts: Okay, this pudding is seriously a game changer. There's something about waiting the 5 minutes to re-whisk your mixture that makes it thick and creamy and perfect. Chia seeds hit you with omega-3 fatty acids, antioxidants, and fiber. Not to mention, these baby seeds are a seriously filling protein source. They're a perfect snack for pre workout, mid-morning, afternoon, after dinner…. Okay, okay, they're perfect literally any time of day. Feel free to experiment with toppings on this sweet treat and get creative!

Sweet Potato Brownies

- 1 cup mashed cooked sweet potato
- ½ cup nut butter
- 2 Tablespoons maple syrup
- ¼ cup cocoa powder
- Optional: ½ cup chocolate chips or cacao nibs

Preheat your oven to 350 degrees. Line a loaf pan or small square pan with parchment paper and set aside. In a blender, (I love my magic bullet for this!) combine all 4 ingredients and blend until you have a batter consistency. Transfer to your lined pan and bake for 20 min. Remove from oven and allow to cool.

Sarah's Thoughts: You guys, I KNOW it's hard to believe, but these genuinely taste like the brownies your nana made as a kid. The sweet potato gives them a moist, fudgy consistency that is to DIE for, but you can feel confident serving these to anyone, especially as sweet potatoes are known for their fiber, antioxidants, and punches of vitamin A. Sometimes I don't even bake the batter and eat it almost like a thick pudding – with these guys, ANYTHING goes.

Foolproof Banana Bread

Foolproof Banana Bread

- 1 cup mashed bananas
- 2 eggs
- 2 Tablespoons honey
- ¼ cup unsweetened apple sauce
- ¼ cup almond milk
- 1 teaspoon baking soda
- 1 teaspoon vanilla extract
- ½ teaspoon salt
- ½ teaspoon cinnamon
- 1 ¾ cups whole wheat flour
- Optional mix-ins (walnuts, blueberries, raspberries, chocolate chips, etc.)

Preheat oven to 325 degrees. Whisk together applesauce, honey, eggs, bananas, and almond milk. Add baking soda, vanilla, salt, and cinnamon to your mixture. Finally, add your whole wheat flower until mixture is entirely combined. Add any mix-ins and bake for 55 min for a loaf (9x5 is your best size choice!) or bake for about 25 min muffin style!

Sarah's Thoughts: Let's be honest – there are a LOT of banana bread recipes out there. And they all have a time and a place. This recipe blows me away because it comes out perfectly Every. Time. Seriously, I think I have forgotten to add banana before and somehow they still magically turned out! They freeze BEAUTIFULLY so they're a perfect thing to have in the freezer and top with peanut butter (hello?! Decadence, I tell you!) when you're short on time but really craving a homemade treat. And on top of everything else, there's no added oil here, and the bread is perfectly dense while still moist so you'll walk away from these muffins feeling full and just... exceptionally happy.

Sweet Potato Brownies

- 1 cup mashed cooked sweet potato
- ½ cup nut butter
- 2 Tablespoons maple syrup
- ¼ cup cocoa powder
- Optional: ½ cup chocolate chips or cacao nibs

Preheat your oven to 350 degrees. Line a loaf pan or small square pan with parchment paper and set aside. In a blender, (I love my magic bullet for this!) combine all 4 ingredients and blend until you have a batter consistency. Transfer to your lined pan and bake for 20 min. Remove from oven and allow to cool.

Sarah's Thoughts: You guys, I KNOW it's hard to believe, but these genuinely taste like the brownies your nana made as a kid. The sweet potato gives them a moist, fudgy consistency that is to DIE for, but you can feel confident serving these to anyone, especially as sweet potatoes are known for their fiber, antioxidants, and punches of vitamin A. Sometimes I don't even bake the batter and eat it almost like a thick pudding – with these guys, ANYTHING goes.

No Bake Energy Bites

- 1 cup dry rolled oats
- ¼ cup nut butter
- ¼ cup honey
- 1 banana
- Mix ins of choice. My personal faves:
    - 2 Tablespoons hemp seeds
    - 2 Tablespoons chia seeds
    - 1 Tablespoon cacao powder
    - Cacao nibs
    - Chocolate chips
    - Coconut shreds
    - Raspberry extract

Mix oats, almond butter, and honey in a large bowl. Mash the banana and add it to the bowl. Add any mix ins. Refrigerate for an hour. Mold into bite sized balls and continue to refrigerate.

Sarah's Thoughts: Okay this is about as basic as an energy bite recipe gets. And you can get CRAZY here, or keep it basic. I love having these on hand for a quick grab before a morning workout or an after dinner mini treat. Sometimes, I'll make the basic recipe and then divide it into 4 bowls, and then throw different toppings in each to see which I like best and have an assortment on hand. There's no wrong approach with these little honeys!

Everly's Favorite Brownies

Everly's Favorite Brownies

- ¼ cup melted coconut oil
- ½ cup unsweetened cocoa powder
- 3 Tablespoons maple syrup
- 2 large room temperature eggs
- 1 teaspoon vanilla
- ¼ cup coconut flour
- ½ teaspoon salt
- ¼ teaspoon baking soda
- 1 Tablespoon hot water blended with 1 teaspoon instant coffee (This is the secret ingredient you guys!!)

Preheat oven to 350 degrees. Line an 8x8 baking pan with parchment paper or spray with coconut oil. Mix warm melted coconut oil, cocoa powder, and maple syrup. Allow to cool for approx. 5 minutes and then add eggs, vanilla, and coffee. Add in your coconut flour, salt, and baking soda. Mix and pour into pan. Allow to cool completely in the tray (about 20 minutes) and try not to eat them all in one sitting!

<u>Sarah's Thoughts:</u> I could write a love letter about these babies. Seriously, I teared up when I finally perfected this recipe. And if you don't trust me, Everly, my favorite one year old, is a TOUGH critic and I am grateful she gave us the thumbs up here! I love making them in square muffin tins so they are individually sized… Sometimes I forget that the 8x8 pan isn't an individual muffin too…

Everly and Her Favorite Brownies!

Can't Stop Won't Stop

Dessert Platter with Doesn't-Get-Simpler Peanut Butter Cookies, Chocolate Dipped Strawberries, and Lemon Sugar Cookie Drops

Lemon Sugar Cookie Drops

- 1 1/3 cups Almond Flour
- 2 Tablespoons coconut flour
- ¼ cup honey
- ½ teaspoon baking soda
- ¼ cup lemon juice
- ¼ cup coconut oil
- 1 Tablespoon lemon zest

Preheat oven to 350 degrees. In a bowl, combine all dry ingredients (almond flour, coconut flour, baking soda). In a separate bowl, combine melted coconut oil, honey, and lemon juice. Combine the wet and dry ingredients and add lemon zest. Your batter should be soft and not too dry. Wrap your dough in plastic wrap and refrigerate for 10 min. Remove from fridge and roll dough into 8 small cookies. These will not spread out in the oven, so feel free to press them down. However, the thicker the cookie the softer they will be! Bake for 15 min. Allow the cookies to cool for 20 min before removing from your baking sheet!

Sarah's Thoughts: Fun Fact: The town I was born and raised in, (Upland, CA) holds a lemon festival every year. The town was built on lemon and orange groves, and the people of upland are PROUD of their heritage. My parents have lemon trees in their front yard and during the summer, we can't give them away fast enough. It wasn't until I moved away, and saw people BUYING lemons in the grocery stores that I realized not everyone has constant access to the freshest, best lemons in the world. Broke my heart! But, making these cookies seals the hole just a tiny bit. They are soft on the inside and crunchy on the outside. If I'm feeling REALLY crazy, I'll add a teaspoon of my World's Easiest Jam (Page 67) to the center to give it just a tiny bit of another flavor. But honestly, these are the perfect after dinner palette cleanser.

Easy Berry Oat Crumble

- 2 cups of frozen berries
- 1/2 cup rolled oats
- 1 teaspoon cinnamon
- 1 Tablespoon honey or maple syrup
- ½ teaspoon nutmeg
- 1/4 cup chopped walnuts
- 1 Tablespoon melted butter

Preheat oven to 375 degrees. Pour your frozen berries into two small oven safe dishes. In a separate bowl, mix oats, cinnamon, honey, nutmeg, walnuts, and melted butter. Top frozen berries with oat crumble and bake for 25-30 minutes or until topping is crispy.

Sarah's Thoughts: It doesn't get better than this healthy take on Dutch pie. And the best part about this recipe is that it's so basic you can absolutely swap in *any* fruit! Try sliced apples, frozen cherries, I've even made a frozen mango crumble before that rocked my world and swapped the walnuts for coconuts! It's a perfect summer night dessert. And if you're looking for a whipped topping, trying hand whisking a jar of full fat coconut milk for a one ingredient whipped cream creation!

Tonycat's Perfect Chocolate Chip Cookies

Sarah's Thoughts: If I had to sum up my philosophy on nutrition and wellness in one sentence it would be: Eat the *insert food here* if it's worth it to you!! These cookies are the ultimate gift in my eyes. They are the perfect mix of chewy and crunchy and you can taste the love in every bite. Do I have them every night? Absolutely not. But they are a definite sweet treat when they come around. And they were brought into my life by my good friend, Anthony Cataldo. His dad is quite literally a chef... so you already know the entire family is trustworthy. You'll notice that this recipe is in metric units – while cooking is an art, baking is a science, and these measurement will
create the tastiest science experiment. I'll let Anthony take it away now...

Ingredients
1 ¼ cups of salted butter (18 Tablespoons)
360 g of all-purpose flour
6 g of baking soda
2 g of baking powder
8 g of sea salt
198 granulated white sugar
133 dark brown sugar
80 light brown sugar
2 large eggs
5 g of pure vanilla extract
250g dark chocolate chips
150g 80% dark chocolate bars (chopped)
Additional sea salt for topping

Begin to melt butter in the pot on medium-low heat. Keep stirring so the butter doesn't burn. You will know it has browned when you see small brown specks in the bottom of the pot, and there is an overwhelming nutty aroma coming off the butter. Once the butter has browned, transfer butter to the small bowl. Fill one of the medium bowls with ice and water and place the bowl with the warm butter in the medium bowl to cool. In one of the medium bowls, combine flour, baking soda, baking powder, and sea salt. Whisk to combine. Once the butter has cooled, pour into the liquid measuring cup. Make sure there is 1 cup of butter (if there is less, top with water until it reaches one cup). In the large bowl, add the sugars. Whisk to combine. Add cooled butter. Cream together with spatula. Once combined, beat in eggs and vanilla until fluffy. Add dry ingredients in 2 increments until combined. Add chocolate. Mix well. On a parchment lined baking sheet, form 2-3 tbs of dough into a ball and place close together. Cover full cookie sheet with plastic wrap, and place into the fridge to set for 24 hours.

~24 hours later ~
Preheat the oven to 375 degrees, bake cookies for 8-10 minutes or until *barely* brown on top. Take out of the oven and top with a generous amount of sea salt. Let cookies cool on the baking sheet for 5 minutes. Enjoy warm cookies with a glass of NON-DAIRY MILK U FOOLS.

Anthony's Thoughts: HELLO!! Tonycat here! These are my absolute favorite cookies in the world. Chocolate chip cookies are one of the most superior desserts this world has to offer, so I decided I would make them even better. This is my spin on your traditional chocolate chip cookie. With the use of browned butter, dark brown sugar, dark chocolate, and sea salt, it gives these cookies a BANG of rich flavor. If you ever end up making these cookies, I would love to know how they turned out; you can reach me on instagram at @anthonyscataldo. Best of luck and hApPy bAkInG!

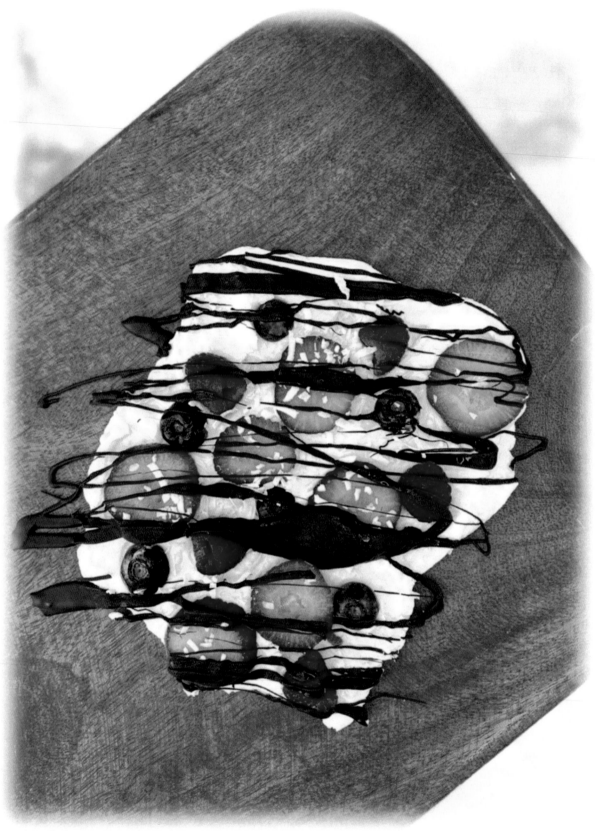

Greek Frozen Yogurt Bars

Greek Frozen Yogurt Bars

- ¾ cup 2% fat Fage plain Greek yogurt
- 1 cup berries
- Natural choco-sauce (page 80)

Roll out parchment paper on a small cookie sheet. Pour Greek yogurt on parchment paper and use the back of your spoon to smooth it out to cover the surface layer. Add berries and drizzle with chocolate. Freeze for 30 minutes. Take mixture off parchment paper, and break of bites for a sweet treat breakfast or dessert!

Sarah's Thoughts: By this point, you know how much I love and adore Greek yogurt. You just can't go wrong! And this recipe is especially lovely because it perfectly balances out a steaming cup of coffee. As ALWAYS, feel free to experiment with your toppings.

Elise's Mug Cake

Elise's Mug Cake

- 1/4 cup oat flour
- 2 Tablespoons cocoa powder
- 1 Tablespoon Maple Syrup
- 1 teaspoon melted butter
- 1 teaspoon vanilla extract
- ¼ teaspoon baking powder
- 1 large egg

Whisk all ingredients together in a large measuring cup. Transfer to mug of choice. Microwave for 1-2 minutes depending on the power of your microwave! I usually do 70 seconds. Enjoy by itself or with toppings of choice!

Elise's Thoughts: Hi! Elise again! This time with DESSERT. If I had to describe myself in 3 words it would be "always craving cake." This cake is ready in minutes and actually nourishes your body. HELLO?! What more could we ask for?

Drinks: Teas and Herbs

The most important note for this section is that the exact dose of any herb *you* need varies from person to person. Experiment with these recipes – and don't be afraid to branch out and try others! Get to know your body and see what makes you feel your best. For example, I love having a cup of cinnamon tea every night after dinner as a signal to my brain and my body that I'm winding down for the night and it's okay to start digesting.

While looking to purchase herbs for the following recipes, be sure and do your research! The average person at the grocery store has no way of knowing the behind-the-scenes production that went into creating that bag of herbs or those prepackaged teas. I find it's best to 1) look for "GMP" on the labels or check out a company's website to ensure they abide by "Good Manufacturing Practice regulations." These are set by the FDA and include identity testing, quality testing, contaminant testing, and cleanliness. And 2) always check those ingredient labels to make sure a packaged herb doesn't include any additives that you don't want in your body!

A Cheat Sheet For Herbal Remedies

Higher Caffeine: Guarana, Kola nut, Coffee, Yerba Mate

Low Caffeine: Black Tea, Chocolate, Green tea, White tea

Balancing/Calming Adaptogens: Maca, Licorice, Reishi mushrooms, Chaga, Ashwaganda, Holy Basil, Gotu Kola, Bacopa, Shatavari

Sleeping/Relaxing: Chamomile, lavender, Linden, Hawthorn, Tart Cherry juice, Warm milk with honey, Skullcap, Kava, Jujube, California Poppy, Melatonin, Valerian

**This is *by no means* an exhaustive list. However, if you're just beginning your journey with herbs, these are the ones I tend to see most often in mainstream grocery stores.

Cinnamon tea

- 2 cinnamon sticks
- 2 cups water

Place the cinnamon sticks and two cups of water in a pot and simmer, covered, for 20 minutes. Enjoy!

Sarah's Thoughts: This tea has become my absolute go to. For the most part, mainstream tea bags are filled with GMOs and can actually cause more harm than good. So, I like to try and get my fix of a warm drink to soothe me in the form of natural recipes. Cinnamon is a hypoglycemic herb that can quickly lower blood sugar and improv insulin sensitivity. It has also been known to relive diabetic neuropathy, promote weight loss, and lower triglyceride and cholesterol levels… HELLO?! Brb, running to start steeping my next cup.

Gut Healing Tea

(I truly WISH there was a better name...)

- 1 teaspoon marshmallow root
- 1 teaspoon plantain
- 1 cinnamon stick
- ½ teaspoon licorice root
- ½ teaspoon rose petals
- 3 cloves
- Pinch of nutmeg

Combine all the herbs in a small pot, and add 2 cups water and bring to a boil. Remove the heat, cover and let simmer for 20 minutes. Strain and let the tea sit, refrigerated, over-night.

Sarah's Thoughts: This tea literally blows my mind. Any time I have a stomach issue, it provides immediate relief. It's helpful for gastritis, ulcers, heartburn, reflux, leaky gut, acid indigestion – really any condition dealing with gastrointestinal issues. It can be a bit intimidating the first time you make it, as the ingredients are not necessarily found in every family pantry, but I promise it'll be worth the investment for how quickly your stomach will feet settled.

Sleepy-Time Tea

- ½ teaspoon lemon balm
- ½ teaspoon passion flower
- ½ teaspoon skullcap
- ½ teaspoon spearmint
- 1 teaspoon honey (add to your liking!)

Combine the herbs in a pot. Pour 4 to 6 ounces of boiling water over them and let them steep, covered, for 20 minutes. Strain and sweeten with honey! Drink immediately.

Sarah's Thoughts: Just like the gut healing tea, this is an investment. HOWEVER, I am a firm believer that it will soothe you to sleep faster than *any* Julie Andrews audiobook (Just me? Okay.) It can also be used as a daytime anti-anxiety tea, but double up the amount of lemon balm. This is a great tea to premix a larger batch and keep on hand.

Amla Magic Tonic

- 1 Tablespoon alma berry powder
- 10 oz water
- Half a fresh lemon
- 1 teaspoon honey

Combine everything in a small pot and bring to a boil. Squeeze the lemon juice into the pot and then throw the peel in as well. Let simmer for 10 min.

Sarah's Thoughts: Okay, I know every mom in the world believes that THEY have the ultimate remedy for colds and sinus infections. But TRUST ME – THIS IS IT. Seriously. I don't know why more people aren't talking about alma berries, but they are MAGIC. They are Indian gooseberries that have been used for centuries as a nutritive tonic, a blood purifier, and have the distinct claim to fame of being the fruit with the highest level of antioxidants in the WORLD. Literally, the vitamin C levels are equal to 20 oranges. HELLO?! It doesn't get better than this concoction – and even though amla berries can be a bit bitter, the lemon and honey balance it right out.

Aloe Vera Spritzer

- 8 ounces aloe Vera juice (check the label to ensure there are no added sugars! I've had the best luck consistently finding it at Trader Joe's!)
- 1 cup fresh watermelon

Pour 8 ounces of aloe vera juice and cup of fresh watermelon into blender. Blend on high for 1-2 min. Optional: Top with sparkling water.

Sarah's Thoughts: I spent far too many years asleep about the amazing abilities of aloe vera juice. This magic elixir contains magnesium, which aids your body with more than 300 enzyme reactions, including those that regulate your blood pressure and heart rhythm. On top of that, it is packed with antioxidants, which help to fight free radicals. Honestly, I could keep going for pages, but trust me that blended with watermelon, you have a hydrating beverage that will keep you feeling refreshed on the inside and outside for days. Bye bye, Aperol Spritz and HELLO Aloe Vera!

Coffee Makes the World Go Around

I am Coffee's #1 fan. Seriously. I don't think I've missed my morning cup of coffee since I was twelve years old. What's not to love about a natural remedy to jump start your day?!

The best part is that nutritional science and recent research even support my love affair! A 2012 study found that people who drank the most coffee had half the risk of liver cancer compared to those who drank the least. In 1986, a group of Norwegian researchers actually discovered that while alcohol consumption was associated with liver damage, coffee consumption was associated with *less* liver inflammation. I'M SOLD. I'll take no further questions!!

In all seriousness, I think coffee gets a bad rap. Companies like Starbucks have capitalized on our human desire for a daily ritual. It's way less fun to walk up to the friendly barista and order "just a tall black coffee please!" than it is to order a "Double mocha frapp hold the whip double the caramel tall in a venti cup!" I felt cool just typing that! What isn't cool is the inevitable sugar crash you'll experience mere hours after consumption. Or the internal damage your gut is experiencing after consuming sugar quantities our ancestors couldn't even conceptualize. Let's take coffee back from big businesses…. Here are some tips for getting that perfect cup without sabotaging your internal gut health!

- Research different types of coffee beans and the flavors that can come from the beans alone. It's becoming more and more trendy for shops to offer coffee bean flavors without adding sugars to the already brewed cup. As much as possible, stay away from added sweeteners. Starbucks has become famous for their crème brûlée holiday lattes and honestly if you're craving crème brûlée, you'd be better off indulging in an actual crème brûlée dessert. Your satiation factor will be higher and your coffee can stay in its purest form.
- The milk or creamer you add should be based on your own body. Personally, I love adding a splash of whole milk to my coffee, as I try to stay away from flavored creamers, and I don't feel a real aversion to dairy. At most coffee shops, their almond/coconut milks will be filled with added sugars, so to avoid any worry, I stick with what's most likely to be unprocessed.
- My best tip for coffee when you just can't drink it without sweetener is to add some flavored extract to your cup. My absolute favorite is raspberry extract. But you'd be surprised how many options there are when you're looking – maple, peppermint, raspberry, vanilla; keep your eyes peeled and add a teaspoon if you're feeling flirty!

Overall Wellness Information

It's easy to get overwhelmed with just how much info is out there on nutrition. And usually articles have varying opinions and science backing them up. I've put together the following pages to essentially be a catch-all: things I love talking to people about or questions I often get asked. Hopefully these will provide you with a quick reference guide, especially as you start to move beyond these recipes and toward creating your own with the knowledge you've gained!

The Great Milk Debate

This is literally the #1 question people ask me. "Seriously, what milk should I be drinking?!" And the lowkey bummer is, <u>there is no absolute correct answer</u>. As with all things in the nutrition world, it really comes down to *your body*. What have you been drinking? What is your exercise level? Do you have a hormone imbalance that you're working through? It's TOUGH to know what's best. Here, I've broken down each type of milk that's usually available to us, and given you some pros and cons for each.

<u>Whole Milk</u> – The list of essential minerals in whole milk is impressive. Calcium. Vitamin A. Vitamin D. Magnesium. It honestly never ends. That being said, a lot of nutritionists have an issue with whole milk mostly because we don't have any way of knowing the quality of life of the cows at the dairy farms. The *Got Milk* campaign of the 90s was entirely paid for by the dairy industry (naturally). As with many things in life, when you follow the money you find the answer to your question. With that in mind, most scientific nutritionists are against dairy milk, as they don't believe the benefits outweigh the potential negatives. There's also the argument that human beings were never meant to consume milk from another species. With all that said, locally sourced milk can be an amazing addition to any diet!

<u>Soy Milk</u> – Soy milk seems to be the overall choice among scientific nutritionists for a couple of reasons. While soy has been a bit demonized in the nutrition world, it offers the highest amount of protein for non-dairy milk options. Soy milk contains all 9 of the essential amino acids we need in our diets, doesn't increase a risk of breast cancer, and contains calcium and iron. That being said, soy allergies are fairly common among the average person and if you're unaware of that, it could cause pretty severe stomach aches. Soy milk manufacturers also tend to add a good amount of sugar to their product so make sure you're double checking that label before heading down the soy milk road!

<u>Almond Milk</u> – The important thing to double check with almond milk is that there is NO added sugar! Almond milk can carry carcinogens that are horrible for our bodies, so it's important to do your research on what brand you're buying and double check that it was sourced in a healthful way. Personally, I like to make my own almond milk, because then I know EXACTLY what's going into it. Almonds are of course a great source of polyunsaturated fats, so watching my almonds blend with water gives me confidence that my body is getting all the goods. The main pro of almond milk is how low it is in calories. That being said, it is ALSO low in protein, so if your main health goal is to lose weight, you'll need to source your calories and protein sources elsewhere in your diet. There is very little fat in almond milk as well, so overall, you're really just getting water with a bit of flavor to it. As long as there is no sugar added (like Starbucks almond milk has!), there's nothing wrong with that – but make sure you understand why you're choosing almond milk.

<u>Oat Milk</u> – Relatively new on the milk scene, oat milk is great for cereals, hot beverages, and drinking on its own. The most important facts about oat milk to remember are that 1) it probably won't sit well with you if your body has an aversion to grains or gluten and 2) it is a carb. Even though it comes in liquid form, those carbohydrates are alive and well. The sugar in it is natural, and the calories are high, but it does provide more riboflavin (vitamin b-2) than regular cow's milk. I love oat milk as long as I use it as a balanced part of my nutritional day.

<u>Coconut Milk</u> – I've found coconut milk to be insanely polarizing, mostly because of the taste. I personally LOVE the taste of coconut – I think it gives a nice sweet undertone to my smoothies and is perfect for sweetening my coffee. It's a great source of Medium-Chain Triglycerides, contains antimicrobial properties, including antiviral, antibacterial, and anti-fungal elements to boost your immune system, and contains numerous antioxidants. That said, the protein levels are almost non-existent, it often contains guar gum, which might cause digestive issues for some people, and Carrageenan is often used to thicken the coconut milk. As I've said (probably too many times at this point) know the risks and benefits – and then make an informed decision on if coconut milk is a fit for your lifestyle!

Hopefully, this gives you some insight into the vast world of milk options, and you feel empowered to make a decision about which you like best! Honestly, I'm sure my bias shined through on this page, because I've spent so much time figuring out which milk works for my body and which benefits seem most important in my day to day! Unfortunately, no one can make those decisions for *you*.

When I'm at home, I usually have 4 types of milk on hand at all times. Overkill? I don't know, only God can judge me I guess. I defend myself, however because each milk plays such a different role in my dishes. For example, if I'm having cereal, I don't need to use oat milk because it's basically another carb source and I'm already getting plenty of carbs from the cereal alone. In that case, I'll go with almond milk. But if I'm having 2 eggs for breakfast and I'm craving a carb source, I'll definitely reach for oat milk because I personally think it froths the best! My dad has had a glass of 2% dairy milk with his dinner every single night since he was 2 years old, and without it, his body would definitely feel strange for a while! He has no allergy to dairy, so why should he change that habit? I personally urge you to not let the world shame you for your milk choice – <u>but</u> inform yourself so you can make the best decision(s) for *your* body!

Recommended Supplements:

Personally, I make sure I have 5 supplements with me at all times. They are:

- **Coq10** – AKA ubiquinol, is an antioxidant. When ubiquin*ol* extinguishes a free radical, it is oxidized to ubiquin*one*. To act as an effective antioxidant again, the body must regenerate ubiquinol from ubiquinone. Think of it like an electrical fuse: Ubiquinol can only be used once before having to be reset. Sunlight and chlorophyll can help to fuel this process. To put this super simply: CoQ10 helps to rebuild our cells. Our body produces it naturally, and we get it through many different commonly consumed fruit and vegetables.
- **Vitamin D** – The best way to get vitamin D into your body is through direct sunlight. Of course, vitamin D is also found in a multitude of vegetables and supports immune health and muscle function. It most commonly affects our T and B cells to aid in fighting unknown disease cells when they enter our bodies.
- **A Probiotic** – I cannot write enough positive words about probiotics. They help to keep our gut bacteria in check and can be vital to balancing out your internal gut bacteria when you are taking any sort of antibiotic. Our gut is commonly referred to as our "second brain" because it has its own enteric nervous system that consists of billions of neurons. It's literally filled with the same kinds of neurotransmitters found in the brain in our skulls!! I think that's worth taking extra good care of!
- **Oregano oil** – Oregano oil literally kills unwanted bacteria in our body. I keep it around for when I start to feel a tickle in my throat or even when I start to feel a migraine coming on. That being said, too much oregano oil taken in a short time frame can start to have a negative impact on your liver and kidneys – so remember, as always, more isn't always better!!
- **Amla Powder** – Amla powder is a powdered Indian berry that has the most antioxidants of any berry in the world. I like to keep a couple of homemade amla powder pills with me and start taking them at the sign of a minor cold or infection. Check out my Amla Magic Tonic on page 111 for more info on this magic berry!

Sarah's Thoughts on Supplements: While the FDA *tries their best* to keep track of the supplement industry, it really isn't regulated very well. It's difficult to make sure that branded supplements are really providing what they say they are and aren't adding scary chemicals in there. I personally like to really focus on my nutrition and getting my nutrients through whole foods. Call me a control freak, but I also love physically knowing what food I put in my mouth, and then noting the effects they seem to have on my health, rather than consuming a pill and hoping for the best (or even just hoping for a placebo effect!)

With that said, I do like to keep the previously mentioned supplements on hand to help my body out a bit when I know I wasn't able to set it up for success. (For example, if I'm traveling all day and know that I won't get much sunlight or kale in my lunch, I'll take a vitamin D pill at bed time to make sure my body can use it!) Our bodies are BRILLIANT – they know what vitamins we need to survive and thrive, and they know what nutrients to hold on to so we remain healthy.

Give your body a strong foundation and I think you'll find pretty quickly that your nightly gummy vitamin was really just a mental placeholder for a late-night fruit sugary snack.

Spice up Your Life!!

An Interlude by Peter Michael Jordan

Sarah's thoughts: As I've mentioned before, one of my favorite things about the world of food is the bonds it creates! Peter was one of my first nutrition clients, and would constantly update me about new spices he was trying on my recipes. Nothing brings me more joy than knowing a flavor profile was brought to the next level! I asked him to guest-write this page on spices for you, as he's become my go-to guru for every question centered around upping my holistic health game WITHOUT compromising flavor!

Hello Hello Hello! I'm one of Sarah's good friends who, like you, is entering this world of holistic eating!! While it's exciting and fun to learn about, it can absolutely be daunting. Sarah helped be through my journey, and helped me find the best way to fuel my body. I'm so happy I learned how to partake in this tasty, fuel producing extrAHvAHgAHnzAAAHHHHHhhh, darling!

That being said, I would be remiss if I didn't mention my deep, **deep,** love of FOOD. Cooking (eating) is a major passion of mine, and I love experimenting with Sarah's recipe's and tuning them to my tastebuds. Pre-Sarah, (or, P.S. as I like to say) I was all about salt – the more salt, the better the taste, right?!! How wrong I was. A.S. (After Sarah) was when I starting using other techniques to add flavor to my food. And what was the biggest lesson I learned? Acid, acid, ACID!! The right acids are your friend on this journey. What to shush up your hummus? Add lemon! It's going to give you that exciting/satisfying sensation you crave from salt without the bloat we all hate. Other acids like red wine, apple cider, and rice vinegar are all commonly added acids as well!

On the opposite side of the spectrum, we come to our good friends: the natural sweeteners. The additions you need to cut through those acidic, pungent flavors. Things like agave, honey, and my personal favorite: 100% natural maple syrup. A mix of one of these, a vinegar, and a dash of mustard quickly gives you a simple vinaigrette fit for a king!

Now that we're clear on the basics,

let's talk about really flirting with the devil.

Getting a little dangerous.

Tempting our inner wild child.

I like a spicier dish – which leads to my dad saying my dishes have a "ZIP!" to them before he even tastes it. Some of my favorite spices are of course cayenne, chili powder, cumin, paprika, pepper, and chili flakes. I add chili flakes to almost everything I cook. It adds little to no *flavor,* but all the spice you want. By adding flakes, you're not altering the integrity of the dish, but complimenting the already present flavors. Cayenne, on the other hand, is a bit more temperamental... some could say a little HOT headed.... Should I show myself out the same way I came in? Great, thanks for having me!! JOKES ASIDE, Cayenne is simply HOT and great for southern Asian cooking and Latin inspired dishes. Then there's of course paprika, which can take on different flavors in your dish – Smoked paprika is a great tool to discover a more smokey, and dare I say, bacon-y flavor to a tofu marinade. The world is your oyster when it comes to invigorating those sweet, sweet glands through your food.

Finally, I want to quickly remind you of the fun, experimental side of these ingredients. Try some Italian herbs in your morning scramble. Bake your sweet potato with a little cayenne and garlic powder. Get adventurous, and try all the different combos your heart desires. There's no absolute RIGHT way to spice up your life!

P.S. If you have access to FRESH herbs, GO OFF! Dive in! Grow them yourself!! Rosemary, sage, thyme, basil, green onions! Get funky and fresh – they make a WORLD of difference, henny!

Spices-as-Medicine Cheat Sheet:

1. Cinnamon

   Main Pros: Immediately lowers your blood sugar. It gives a sweet flavor to your food and may provide heart healthy benefits like reducing high blood cholesterol and triglyceride levels.
   Quick Use? Try sprinkling it on yogurt, fruit, your morning oats - cinnamon might be the ONLY thing in the holistic healthy world I don't think you can overdo!

2. Cayenne:

   Main Pros: Eases joint pain! This specific type of chili pepper contains capsaicin, which reduces the number of pain signals sent to your brain. Basically, when you consume cayenne, your brain doesn't receive the message that there is discomfort. It can help with arthritis and diabetes related joint damage. It can also benefit those struggling with ulcers, as it balances the bacteria that has infiltrated your gut.
   Quick Use? You can easily add cayenne to any chilis, soups, salad dressings, you name it! I love adding a splash to my tea to balance out a lemon/ginger feel!

3. Ginger

   Main Pros: Relieves nausea. It's remarkably effective at aiding stomach aches and may even help to fight some aggressive forms of cancer. It's helpful in working with your T and B cells when they start to fight infection as well.
   Quick Use: Ginger may be the most convenient spice of all. It's readily available in powder form or in its whole form. If you buy it in its whole form, it's easiest to slice or grate it. You can easily use it in vegetable stir frys, in your tea, or in salad dressings.

4. Garlic

   Main Pros: Boosts Heart Health. Keeps vampires away. (I'm kidding about the second one but HONESTLY you can never be too careful). Garlic is especially helpful for women, as intake can help keep blood vessels flexible and can reduce cholesterol. As you age, your arteries begin to harden, as fatty deposits build up. Smoking, high blood pressure, and high cholesterol can speed up this process and lead to scary narrow arteries. Garlic however, helps to slow down this process tremendously.
   Quick Use: I love to use garlic in just about any savory dish. Pair it with olive oil and rosemary and your vegetables are suddenly worthy of a Michelin restaurant. Add it to soups, salad dressings... the list goes on and on.

5. Turmeric

Main Pros: Fights inflammation. Turmeric is mostly made up of curcumin, and there has been much research around the idea that it can reduce inflammation in the brain – inflammation in the brain is what leads to Alzheimer's and depression, so you can see the benefits! It can also reduce high blood cholesterol and swelling in many adults. It's great to up your turmeric levels after a heavy workout, or when you start to feel any sort of swelling or sickness in your throat!
Quick Use: Use it as a rub for vegetables or meats, tofu, or sprinkle some in your banana/mango smoothie!

6. Peppermint

Main Pros: Relieves Nausea and IBS. Peppermint is an extremely oily herb, so it works to relax muscles in the colon. This often helps to aid those suffering from issues with an unclean gut.
Quick Use: I love boiling peppermint in hot water, similar to the cinnamon tea on page 108. But you can also add some to your morning coffee for Christmas in a cup! (Trust me on this one)

7. Basil

Main Pros: Helps boost immune system. While most herbs and spices help to aid the immune system, basil can also inhibit the growth of a range of bacteria, yeasts and molds.
Quick Use: I like to throw a couple basil leaves in my smoothies to give them an earthier flavor, but basil quickly livens up just about any savory dish!

8. Sage

Main Pros: Improves brain function and memory. Alzheimer's disease is accompanied by a drop in the level of acetylcholine, a chemical messenger in the brain. Sage inhibits the breakdown of acetylcholine, so it has been known to help both young and old with memory related issues.
Quick Use: I love adding sage to my pasta dishes. You can toss it with olive oil and vegetables before roasting to give you a balanced burst of flavor in your meal!

Top 10 Things I love in my Kitchen

- **Air Fryer –** Air Fryers are an amazing investment *especially* if you are cooking for one. I love to throw my veggies in the air fryer for 20 min with some olive oil, salt, and pepper - and dinner is SERVED baby. An air fryer gives you all the benefits of an oven but with a quicker delivery time and no "UGH I forgot to preheat the oven" moments.
- **Air Popper –** Popcorn, in my informed opinion, is one of the greatest joys of life. And while the packaged version of popcorn can lead to unwanted chemicals and cancer aiding agents, an air popper gives you the purest form of corn. I love how quickly you can have fresh popcorn and you can dress is however you'd like! Air poppers are a small investment (usually around $15) and bring night after night of joy in the form of a quick, healthy snack when you just need a little something. (I personally love topping mine with a Tablespoon of ghee and some nutritional yeast.)
- **Fruit Storage container** - If I could only eat one food for the rest of my life it would be raspberries. So, I like to make sure I always have raspberries, strawberries, blackberries, and blueberries washed and in a fruit storage container for easy access. Instead of reaching for a wrapped candy, reach for your berry bowl!
- **Oil Spray –** Oil spray is great to have on hand for sautéing just about anything you can imagine. I start every pan with a quick spray of ghee or coconut oil to avoid sticking. I think the spray oils help us stick to my favorite phrase: *Less is more!* (I try to limit my olive oil to be just a topping or dressing, as it can actually become dangerous to our health when consumed after being cooked at high temperatures!)
- **Measuring spoons/cups –** *Especially* when it comes to baking, there's nothing more vital than a set of measuring spoons/cups that you LOVE. Make sure they're easily accessible and easy to clean, since they're getting a daily workout!
- **Blender/Magic Bullet –** There's no getting around it: a good blender is vital in every kitchen. Does that mean you need to go buy the $600 Vitamix?! Absolutely not. I've had my Amazon $80 blender for 4 years and she hasn't let me down yet! But do your research and know what you'll be using your blender for. Personally, I'm usually making smoothies and smoothie bowls, but my blender has the ability to blend up a solid bowl of hummus or Jalapeño Crème as well. I also love my magic bullet to travel with, or to whip up smaller batches of dressings or hummus.
- **Organization Station –** The best trick I know to eating healthy and whole foods is to have everything you need to succeed at your fingertips. I grabbed a bunch of storage containers on Amazon to keep on hand filled with: Hemp hearts, unsweetened coconut flakes, chia seeds, cacao powder, maca powder, cacao nibs, bee pollen, and grounded flax seeds. They all have their handy containers and I store them near my blender – it makes it that much easier to add extra nutrients to your smoothies, oatmeal, yogurt bowls… you get the idea!
- **Reusable Ice Cream container –** I found my reusable ice cream storage container at TJ Maxx for $1.99. I love to make banana nice cream and keep this in the freezer so I don't feel left out when I see anyone reaching for a pint of Ben and Jerry's!
- **Glass Storage Containers –** Seriously, storage containers have saved me on more than one occasion. As usual, I don't believe that more is better. Find 6 storage containers you LOVE in all different sizes and make it a point to use up food in those containers before they go bad! I also like to make sure I keep frozen bananas in a container at all times for easy smoothie and nice cream action.
- **Tabletop Oil Mister –** I found mine at TJ Maxx for $3.99! I love to put my homemade dressings in the mister and leave it on the table. They're a great way to enjoy your homemade, olive oil-based dressing without sabotaging flavor or convenience for your or guests in your home.

Fruits, Veggies, and Their Seasons

One of my favorite things about eating a holistically balanced diet is getting to follow the seasons and what's going to be the ripest during any given month of the year. The main tip I usually offer people is that the more COLOR the better. If a fruit or veggie gives off a really deep, stunning shade of any color, it holds more antioxidants. There's a reason we are drawn to the deeeeep red, juicy strawberries at the farmer's market - They are literally better for us and our immune systems. I hope this quick cheat sheet will help you remember which fruits and veggies to be experimenting with during each month of the year!

Winter (January, February, March):

- Beets
- Brussel sprouts
- Grapefruit
- Kiwi fruit
- Leeks
- Lemons
- Oranges
- Parsnips
- Pears
- Potatoes
- Pumpkin
- Rutabagas
- Sweet potatos and yams
- Winter Squash

Spring (April, May, June):

- Apricots
- Asparagus
- Broccoli
- Green Beans
- Mangoes
- Mushrooms
- Peas
- Radishes
- Rhubarb
- Spinach
- Strawberries
- Swiss Chard

Summer (July, August, Sept):

- Avocados
- Bel Peppers
- Berries
- Cantaloupe
- Cherries
- Corn
- Cucumbers
- Eggplant
- Green Beans
- Honeydew Melon
- Kiwi Fruit
- Okra
- Peaches
- Plums
- Summer Squash
- Tomatoes
- Watermelon

Fall (October, November, December):

- Apples
- Beets
- Broccoli
- Cauliflower
- Cranberries
- Grapes
- Kale
- Mushrooms
- Parsnips
- Pears
- Potatoes
- Pumpkin
- Sweet potatoes and yams
- Turnips
- Winter squash

Recommended Readings

As always, if you have additional questions, don't be afraid to reach out! Let's discuss – and if I don't know, my guilty pleasure is researching scientific nutritional studies. I think it's <u>vital</u> to read different opinions, as so many doctors, dieticians, and nutritionist offer varying information. Remember, all bodies are different (do I sound like a broken record yet?), so be aware that what works for someone else may not work for you. Any nutritionist I trust the research from usually says this blatantly. If YOU'RE looking to up your personal awareness, here are some books I loved learning from.

- <u>The Disease Delusion</u>
  - By Dr. Jeffrey S. Bland

- <u>Staying Healthy with the Seasons</u>
  - By Elson Haas M.D.

- <u>How To Not Die</u>
  - By Michael Greger (Michael Greger also has a website where he posts daily nutritional videos with topics he's researching all for FREE. Check it out… but be prepared to lose hours to a deep youtube rabbit hole!)
  - Nutritionfacts.org

- <u>The Whole Foods Diet: The Lifesaving Plan for Health and Longevity</u>
  - By John Mackey; Alona Pulde, M.D., and Matthew Lederman, M.D.

- <u>The Mind Gut Connection</u>
  - Emeran Mayer, M.D.

- <u>Food Isn't Medicine</u>
  - By Dr. Joshua Wolrish

- <u>The Omnivore's Dilemma</u>
  - By Michael Pollen

Thank you!

From the bottom of my heart (stomach? Yeah, let's go with stomach), thank you for reading this introduction to Holistic Nutrition and wellness. I hope you feel like you have a friend walking alongside you on this journey to well-being. Of course, with any lifestyle change, it can be scary at times! Human beings are creatures of habit, and change, in any amount can be tough.

My biggest piece of advice would be to *start small.* One choice at a time. Make the next best choice *for you.* Listen to your body as you start to identify your own personal hunger cues and what your body is craving to succeed. I fully believe that as you retrain your body to crave nutrient dense, unprocessed foods, "making healthy choices" becomes less of a choice and more a natural response. Remember, this is a low stakes approach. Don't concern yourself too much with any setbacks. Our bodies, our minds, and our guts are strong and can make it through a LOT.

You are a strong, resilient, beautiful human being and your body can do AMAZING things. Start treating your body like it belongs to the person you love most in the world and your mindset will follow suit! And remember, you are *never* alone! Reach out to a close friend! A sibling! Reach out to ME!! I would love to be a listening ear for a new recipe or a grocery store find you just scored!

Let's stick together on this journey to nutritional wellness, and keep it ALL *low stakes.*

Never Ending Thanks to...

Tyler Logan – There aren't enough words to convey how grateful I am for your friendship, creative eye, and your never-ending talent to make anything beautiful. Collaborating with you on each new project is dreamy. I love you.

Bob and Pam Logan. Matt, Lauren, and Everly Bodkin – For making me feel so at home in your kitchen and for believing in this crazy project. And an extra special shout out to your white dishes! And, of course, to LaLa for rounding out the best tasting crew.

My ENTIRE editing team - (My dad).

Peter Michael Jordan - For being my FIRST official nutrition client and loving nutrition and recipes as much as I do. You're going to the Prom, Barry!

Morgan Reynolds – For ALWAYS making magic and making it work. My love, my light. Hustle Hustle Hustle.

Elise Vannerson, Mary Elizabeth Drake, Delphi Borich, Anthony Cataldo, Mama Jacqui, Maggie and Austin Brion, and Peter Michael Jordan - For your perfect additional recipes.

Bruce and Barb - For seeing the positives in recipe experiments gone awry.

Mom and Dad - For being the most honest taste test crew in the world, and the best support system for every new adventure.

YOU! For trusting me with your nutritional journey!

Made in the USA
Columbia, SC
31 May 2021